There he was, a giant figure of a man, who brushed the trees out of his way like stalks of grass

Paul Bunyan
and His Great Blue Ox

Retold by
WALLACE WADSWORTH

Illustrated by
ENRICO ARNO

Doubleday & Company, Inc.
Garden City, New York

Contents

[5]

13684

CONTENTS

ILLUSTRATIONS

There he was, a giant figure of a man, who brushed the trees out of his way like stalks of grass

Paul Bunyan

and His Great Blue Ox

I

The Hero of the Lumber Woods

IN the lumber woods the winter night has settled down over the snowy forest land. The trees crackle with the cold, the ice of the lakes booms and creaks harshly in the rending grip of the frost, and far to the north those ever-restless dancers, the Northern Lights, leap and climb the sky in flickering waves of green and purple and crimson. The air stings the skin and prickles the nostrils, and no creature braves its chill save the fur-clad forest animals that slip hungrily along, restless and unseen shadows, among the trees.

Only in the big lumber camp is there sign of warmth and comfort. There, in bunkhouse and shanty, the men have gathered together after their hard labors of the day, enjoying the companionship of one another and perhaps playing crude jokes, boasting of past deeds, or looking on laughingly while one of their number tests the mettle of another in some feat of strength. But most likely they are doing what they like best to do on a night like this, when the wind groans and whistles around the buildings and the frost noises crackle and jeer, and that is to sit back and listen while the old-timers tell over again the wonderful tales of Paul Bunyan and his marvelous deeds.

Paul Bunyan! the mightiest man that ever came into the woods! Never do woodsmen tire of hearing of him. Never do the stories of his tremendous labors grow old to them, for not only was he the first one of all their kind, but he was also the greatest lumberjack that ever lived, the hero of them all.

Paul Bunyan! the first and greatest logger! He is really the father of logging as it is to-day, for all the best methods for logging off timber were developed by him and have been in use ever since. Not only that, but he also invented all the tools that are used by lumberjacks even today: the double-bitted ax, the grindstone, the crosscut saw, the peavy, and all the others. A very great genius was Paul, a remarkable man in every way and one well fit to be the hero of all woodsmen who have come after him.

It has been long since anyone has seen him face

to face, though now and then some old-time lumberjack will admit that he has worked for Paul in one or another of his smaller camps, or that he has a friend who once knew Paul personally. It is from such men as these that the stories of the great logger's exploits have come, and since these tales of him are first-hand, so to speak, they are therefore of unquestionable truth.

Paul Bunyan was of tremendous size and strength, the strongest man that ever swung an ax. Now a lumberjack always measures things by ax-handles instead of by feet or yards—a thing will be so many ax-handles long or so many ax-handles high—and the various estimates as to Paul's size are given in this way. Accordingly, the estimate which seems most nearly correct is that Paul was so big that ninety-seven ax-handles would just barely measure him from hip to hip. This estimate is a little misleading, however, as no one is sure whether the ordinary ax-handle is meant, or one of Paul's, which was seven—or perhaps it was seventy—times as long as the ordinary one. At any rate, it can easily be seen that he was no little fellow.

He had curly black hair which his loving wife used to comb for him every morning with a great crosscut saw, after first parting it nicely with a broadax, and a big black beard that was as long as it was wide and as wide as it was long. He was rather proud of this beard, and took great care of it. Several times every day he would pull up a young pine tree by the roots and use its stiff branches in combing and brushing it smooth.

Paul was so strong that he never did things as other men did them. That is what Joe Mufraw discovered once when he came looking for Paul, intending to get into a fight with him. Joe also was a very big man and a great bully, always looking for a fight. One by one he had whipped the best fighters in all the logging camps around, until by the time the big drive was over in the spring he claimed to be the boss bully and the mightiest fighter in the woods. It was then that someone told him about Paul Bunyan, and Joe straightway set off to find him. As he went along he kept boasting more and more, telling everyone he met of all the fearful things he would do to Paul when finally he found him.

The winter's logging work being done, Paul was at his farm, getting his land ready for spring planting, and when Joe discovered him he was plowing a piece of recently cleared land with five yokes of oxen. Joe threw off his coat and watched the plow come nearer and nearer, its share cutting and slicing its way through great stumps and mighty bowlders as if they were not there. When

Paul reached the end of the field, instead of letting his oxen take the time to turn themselves around he just picked them up, all ten of them, and set them down again headed in the other direction without any delay or trouble. It was not until then that he noticed Joe.

"Well, stranger," he hailed in a mighty voice that made Joe's ears ring, "what can I do for you?"

But Joe didn't answer. With a stunned expression on his face, he backed away from the field and turned and stumbled along the path he had come. "Ox an' all!" he kept muttering to himself, shaking his head as if the very thought made him dizzy. "He picks up ox an' all! No, no! No fights with that man for Joe!" And so it happened that the big contest never did occur, and Joe Mufraw was never heard of again.

It is pretty hard to give a definite date to any of the mighty deeds which Paul Bunyan performed, as only one guidepost as to time is given in all the stories that have been told of him and his exploits. This guidepost, as one may call it, is the definite mention of the winter of the Blue Snow. The snow that fell during that winter was a bright, glistening blue in color, very interesting and attractive at first, but soon growing so tiresome to the eyes that every one was longing for the sight of some common, old-fashioned white snow again. Paul set out to find some, but he had to go clear to China before he finally found what he was looking for.

Now it is certain that all that the great logger ever did took place either before or after the falling of the Blue Snow, and so—if it were only possible to discover the exact year during which the Blue Snowstorm occurred—all the things he did could be dated forward or backward from that time, and the definite date of their occurrence established in that way.

It is thought quite probable that the Blue Snow fell during the Year of the Two Winters, when it grew so cold that it didn't start to thaw until after it began to freeze again. They had winter all summer that year, and then in the fall it turned colder. It was so cold that one night when Paul set the coffee-pot out of doors to cool, the coffee froze so quickly that the ice was hot.

At any rate, one thing is sure, and that is that Paul Bunyan did all the mighty deeds which are told of him. It is not nearly so important to know *when* he did them as to know that they actually did happen. Nor did he wait until he was a man full grown before showing the remarkable qualities that were in him, for even as a baby he was fully as exceptional as when he reached manhood.

II

The Young Paul

MANY, many years have passed since Paul Bunyan was born. In fact, so long ago has it been that no one knows just who his parents were, though it is said that his father was a fine, upstanding man of great strength and his mother a sturdy lass from one of the French-Canadian provinces. Whoever they were, they must have been very proud of their lusty son, as well they might be. His birthplace is said to have been somewhere along the northern coast of Maine, and the time was long ago, before the Revolutionary War, while England still ruled the Thirteen Colonies.

Paul grew so fast that he was the wonder of people for miles around. When he was only a few weeks old his mother had to fix his bed out of doors, for he had grown so big by that time that he could no longer be taken through the door of his parents' cabin. The out-of-doors air seemed to agree with him, however, and he continued to thrive, until one night he got the colic! Being such a big youngster, there was a very great deal of him to have the colic, as one may well believe, and his pain must have been fully in keeping with his size from the tremendous commotion which he stirred up. All the neighbors for miles around thought they were hearing the roar of a terrific storm and hid in their cellars until it should blow over.

Perhaps his breaking into his father's smokehouse that day had something to do with his illness. The family's winter supply of smoked hams, bacon and salt pork were stored there, but when Paul was discovered, sound asleep in the center of the smokehouse floor, there was not a single ham or side of bacon left in sight. The grease on his hands and face showed pretty surely what had happened to the missing victuals, and as the youngster had only one tooth at the time, he most likely did not give the rich meats the thorough chewing they should have had. At any rate, whether this was the cause of his colic or not, he rolled and kicked and tossed about that night at a prodigious rate, and when morning came it was found that he had destroyed four square miles of standing timber.

As all the trees were fine large ones which his father had been intending to cut and sell to the sawmill as soon as it should be built nearby, he was very angry over the destruction his infant son had caused. "We'll have to do something with that youngster," he said to the child's mother. "Unless we can manage to keep him out of further mischief, in another two or three weeks there won't be a standing tree left in all Maine," and then remembering the disappearance of his hams and bacon the day before, he added, "No, nor a piece of smoked meat, either."

"If we only had a cradle for him," his mother suggested, "then we could tie him in and rock him when he gets restless. Perhaps that would keep him quiet."

"A cradle, eh!" and Paul's father roared with laughter at the very thought. "A cradle! Where could we ever get a cradle for a child that has outgrown a house?"

"Well, I've been thinking about a cradle for him," retorted the mother, "and it seems to me that perhaps you could build him something like a boat. Then we could tie him in it and anchor it out in the water in a safe place, and as long as he is there we needn't worry about his getting into any more mischief."

"Not a bad idea, at all!" her husband exclaimed, really very much pleased with the suggestion. So he called in all of his neighbors to help him cut

the timbers and haul them from the forest to the
biggest shipyard in Eastport. There, all the ship-
builders and carpenters along the coast worked
as hard and as fast as ever they could at building the cradle, and before very long the great log
affair was launched from the ways and anchored
out in the sea. Everyone was very glad when the
task was finished, for all were fearful that some
night Paul might get an even worse attack than
the one he had suffered before and roll about until he destroyed everything in that part of the
country.

So there was the big log cradle at last, floating
near the shore like a big ship at anchor. Great
crowds of people came to see it, for it was the
biggest craft that was ever built in Maine, and
everyone willingly gave a hand toward getting
Paul safely put to bed in it. Even with so many
working together at the task, it took them three
full days to get the husky youngster into his new
cradle and tied there with cables so that he could
not fall out. It was very fortunate for everyone
that the child was feeling well and in the best of
humor, for otherwise he might have resented all
the tugging and pulling which he had to undergo,
and no one knows what fearful calamity might then
have resulted.

At last in the place fixed for him, Paul began to

like the sensation of being rocked by the waves so well that he gave no further trouble for a while, and his parents congratulated themselves upon the excellent arrangement they had made for their lusty son. His father hired a crew of men who were kept busy all the time rowing back and forth between the cradle and the shore, carrying boat-loads of food to him, and altogether Paul was as well satisfied as any child could expect to be.

All went well until one night he got the colic again. It is not known what caused his illness this time, but anyway, he rolled and tossed about so much that he stirred up the sea at a fearful rate. In fact, such a shaking-up did his rolling cradle give the waters that a seventy-foot tide drove up the Bay of Fundy, doing a tremendous lot of damage and even washing away several towns and villages. So high were the waves that they came near to rolling clear across the land and making an island of Nova Scotia!

As a result of this disturbance, the waters have never entirely gone down, and even yet the tide which flows twice each day in the Bay of Fundy is seventy feet high. Anyone, by looking at a map of that part of the Atlantic coast, can easily find where Maine joins Canada and locate the Bay of Fundy, which will prove the truth of the story and show what a mighty child Paul really was.

Naturally, the people who had their homes and property washed away by the great waves which Paul had made were very angry, and they sent a committee to the Governor to make complaint.

"Ahem!" said the Governor, who considered himself a very wise man. "More trouble, eh?" and he frowned gloomily at them. "As if I don't already have enough to worry me, what with the reports I have to make on this and that, the Indians I must guard against and all the very important details I have to take care of in getting ready for the ball I am giving to-morrow night. Hrr-r-rump! Tides, is it? And tides are a part of the sea, aren't they? So I'll just pass this little matter over to the Admiral, who is well trained in all sea affairs. Doubtless he'll be able to stop the tides, if any man can, and locate whatever is causing them."

So it happened, that very same day, that the Admiral got his fleet together, frigates and brigantines and sloops-of-war, and set sail to see what it was all about. He was in a very ill humor, indeed, being greatly displeased at having to miss the Governor's ball, and he swore to be revenged on whatever or whoever was causing him all this trouble.

He cruised about in his flagship, his fleet following him, but never a cause of the disturbance could he find. And the longer he searched, the angrier he became. At last one of the lookouts up in the rigging of the flagship called down that he saw something suspicious off the starboard bow.

"What is it?" roared the Admiral.

"I don't know, sir," called back the lookout. "It looks like a big log barge or scow of some kind, sir. She's anchored near shore, sir, and she's rolling about and kicking up some big waves in a mighty strange manner, sir."

The Admiral ordered the fleet to proceed in the direction the lookout had given, and he seized his spyglass to take a look for himself.

"Why, it's a baby!" he shouted in surprise when the fleet had come nearer. "And sound asleep, too!" he muttered to himself a moment or two later. His mouth dropped open in amazement, for such a baby surely had never been seen by man before. He almost refused to believe his own eyes.

But though Paul was sleeping rather quietly—for him—he still was rocking his cradle about a little. As the ships drew quite near, the Admiral could feel beneath him the force of the waves which the child was stirring up as he moved about in his slumber.

He suddenly began to get quite angry again. The idea! Sending him traipsing off over the sea and making him miss the Governor's ball just to find a sleeping youngster! "Asleep, is he?" he growled. "I'll soon wake him up, all right!" and he called his chief gunner to him. "Fire a broadside over his head," he ordered. "We'll see if that won't make him open his eyes."

The gunners took their places, trained their pieces, and at the word the thirty-six cannon of the frigate's broadside roared out. But Paul was in a very sound slumber, indeed, and the tremendous crash of sound did not so much as make him flutter an eyelid.

"Give him a broadside from all the fleet!" screeched the Admiral, purple with rage at the very thought of such an absurdity. So the guns of all the fleet bellowed and thundered, sending their solid shot whistling close over the floating cradle, and frightening the people on shore so badly that they all ran into the woods to hide, thinking that an enemy was attacking them.

Roar after roar burst from the guns, as broadside followed broadside, but it was almost seven hours before the noise so much as made Paul stir. Then calmly, just as the sound of the last broadside died out, he sat up, rubbed his eyes with chubby fists and yawned.

The red-faced Admiral, in a greater rage than ever by this time, gave the command to fire again. With a great flare of sound, the cannon-balls again whistled over Paul's head. Being asleep, he hadn't noticed them before, and now hearing the terrific crash of the guns for the first time he was startled almost out of his wits. Making a great lunge and snapping the heavy cables which held him in his cradle, he leaped out towards shore, stirring up the water mightily in doing so.

The Admiral's red face suddenly paled with terror. "'Bout ship! Port your helm!" he screamed frantically, and then had no time for further orders. The great waves which Paul had stirred up as he broke loose from his cradle swept down upon the fleet with a fearful roar and tossed the vessels about in a manner fearful to behold. When at last the waters quieted down somewhat, it was found that eight ships had been sunk and much damage wrought upon those that remained.

The Admiral, however, seized the floating cradle as spoils of war and towed it back to port, where eight more warships were built from it. Thus the British Navy was just as well off as it was before, but the Admiral never did forgive Paul for making him miss the Governor's ball.

As for Paul, he reached the shore in safety and vanished into the woods. There he was found by his parents, who had fled thither into hiding as soon as the guns had first begun to roar. Being fearful of punishment for the trouble their infant son had caused, they did not go back to their former home, but slipped quietly away without a word to anyone.

"This boy of ours needs a lot of room," Paul's father growled. "He was never made to live among neighbors."

"Yes," agreed the child's mother. "We'll find a place back in the wilderness, far away from anyone else, where he can play and romp about as he pleases without endangering the lives or property of others." So through the woods they went, just where has never been learned, and deep in virgin country they picked the spot for their new home.

"Why it's a baby!" the Admiral shouted in surprise as the fleet came nearer

III

Paul's Boyhood

THOUGH many of the facts concerning Paul
Bunyan's boyhood are still enshrouded in
mystery, enough are known to show how—from the
very beginning—he began to develop those char-
acteristics which made him so famous in after life.

The first task which confronted Paul's father,
after he had finally found a suitable location for
the new home, was the construction of a house.
This was a tremendous labor for one man to at-
tempt, for this time he planned to build a habi-
tation that would not only accommodate his rapidly growing young son while he remained an
infant but also afford him plenty of growing room
through all the years that must ensue ere he
should reach manhood.

"I am determined that he shall not outgrow his
father's house again," Mr. Bunyan explained to the
boy's mother. "This time I intend to build a cabin
that will shelter him until he is grown and able

to strike out for himself. Why, just think how dangerous it would be to build a house that is just large enough for him now and then have him some night—while he is *inside*—suddenly grow too big for the place! We might never be able to get him out." So he set to work right manfully, hewing down great trees, shaping them and notching them and piling them near at hand until he should be ready to start rearing the walls.

Young Paul, of course, stirred by the insatiable curiosity which was always characteristic of him, crawled and rolled among the chips and shavings where his father worked, taking a great interest in all that was done. His father's tools became his playthings, and never was he happier than when he was able to get hold of a sharp ax and—in his baby way—chip and batter a tough tamarack stump into dust or beaver a great pine log into small pieces. He cut most of his teeth on a broadax, gnawing it so badly out of shape in the process that his father could never use it again. Thus it can readily be seen that his earliest interests were for the things of the woods, and it is not strange that these interests should have persisted and grown stronger through all the years of his life.

His father proceeded apace with the new house, and in a shorter time than one would think he had it completed. Both he and his wife were very proud of it and greatly pleased to know that at last they were again able to have their little son under the same roof with them. It is regrettable that the figures of its dimensions have been lost, for it was in every way a most remarkable structure, fully equal to the task of sheltering a Presidential convention or a six-ring circus—had such things existed in those days—without overtaxing its capacity.

The new home was far from any settlement, but Paul's father believed that he might be able to get in touch with the outside world once more by floating down the river which flowed nearby. Judging that the fine timber which stood so thickly in every direction would bring a good price if only it could be delivered to a mill, he cut down a great many trees, made the logs into a raft, and floated down the river. His experiment was highly successful, and after several weeks he came stalking back through the forest, burdened down with the huge pack of fresh supplies for which he had exchanged his logs. Pleased over finding a market for his timber, he set to work again and soon had a much greater store of logs ready to take to the mill.

Paul, who was by this time big enough so that he had just been put into his first pair of pants, and who was feeling himself quite a man as a consequence, had—as usual—been watching with the greatest interest all that his father did and imitating in his play the labor of his parent. Seeing the great piles of logs which lay beside the river ready for the making of the big raft, he became quite energetic in carrying out a new idea that suddenly stirred him.

When his father came that way shortly afterward, he was struck with the strange change that had taken place. "Where are the logs?" he shouted and called up to the cabin for his wife to come at once. "What can have happened to all the the logs that were piled here?" he asked her in bewilderment, pointing to the empty banks of the stream.

But she was as astonished as he and could not give him the least help in the matter. Then all at once a worried looked came into her eyes, and she turned to him. "And Paul! Where is Paul?" she cried. "He was playing near this very spot just a short while ago!"

"I'll bet that youngster has something to do with my missing logs," growled his father. "I'll soon find him, all right, as he must have drifted downriver with them." So off he started, hurrying along the bank and keeping sharp eyes turned on the stream where he expected every moment to see

some sign of his young son in company with the
disappearing logs. He began to doubt his solution
of the mystery, however, after he had traveled
for many miles and had not yet found the least
evidence of boy or timber having recently come
that way.

Then all at once he knew that he was on the
right track, for a log—one of the missing ones, he
was sure—drifted past him. He was surprised that
it should have come from above him, but back he
turned and hurriedly retraced his steps. He was
beginning to share some of his wife's worries about
their missing son, and he moved along as fast as
his feet would carry him.

It was almost night when he finally overtook
Paul and the logs, far up the river past the cabin.
The child, thinking to imitate his father, had
dumped all the logs into the stream and—in his
unavailing attempts to make them into a raft as he
had seen his father do once before—he had become confused in his directions. As a result, he
had headed up the river instead of in the other
direction and, aided only by a long tough pole,
he had taken the drive upstream against the strong
current. From poling so many logs up over rapids
and waterfalls, the child was very tired when his
father finally caught up with him, and he was quite

willing to abandon his play and trot along home to supper.

As Paul grew a little older, he got into the habit of wandering far away from home, and often his father had to make long searches for him. Finally, in order to make the boy's tracks easy to follow on his future excursions, the parent fixed his son's initials on the bottoms of his shoes with big hobnails. As a result, wherever Paul went he left his mark with every track.

He was so young that he didn't notice this much at first, but nothing ever escaped him long, and when he did discover it he began to get a great deal of fun out of stamping his initials into everything he came to. It was not very long before all the trees, rocks and everything else for miles around bore the evidence of his new sport so that soon it became hard for him to find a place where he could stamp "P. B." without having the new letters become lost among the thousands of earlier sets of his initials.

He was tickled when he finally found a nice, smooth, unmarked surface, even though it was in a somewhat awkward position. He soon discovered how to make use of it, however, and it was a sight well worth seeing to watch him perform his newest stunt. He would stand in the middle of the cabin floor, jump straight up in a sort of flip-flop and stamp "P. B." on the ceiling above where he had just stood. He had to stop doing this one day, sad to relate, on account of the strange disaster which befell him. Seeking to impress his initials on the ceiling extra hard, this time he stamped with such force that he went feet first right on through the ceiling and ripped the roof off the house.

He was very big for his age, of course, but he was never clumsy as many big boys are. Once—the first time he ever went hunting—he sneaked his father's old shotgun out of the house and set forth to see what he could find. He kept his sharp eyes wide open, and at last he saw a deer stick its head around a tree four or five miles away. He blazed away at the animal with the old gun and then was so anxious to see if he had killed it that he started for the spot, lippity-cut. He ran so fast that he outran the load he had fired from the gun, with the result that he got the full charge of buckshot in the seat of his breeches.

So, as one can readily see, his size did not in the least interfere with his spryness. Even when he was an old man, or what would be old for most men, he was so quick on his feet that he could blow out the light in the bunkhouse at night and be in bed and asleep before the room got dark.

As the years of his boyhood went on he continued to get bigger and stronger and quicker of action, as well as becoming better versed in everything that pertained to the woods. He was learning that he seldom dared to exert his full strength, so powerful was he in every way, for fear of the damage he might do. He was only about fourteen or fifteen years old when he found out that he could kill a whole pond full of bullfrogs just with one yell, and as his voice was getting stronger all the time, he had to watch closely and always speak softly, or else the tremendous sound would stun everyone within hearing or perhaps flatten out a few houses.

During the later years that intervened before Paul once more appeared, a grown man in the height of his powers, near the place of his birth along the coast of Maine, he managed to secure two assets: a loving wife, and Babe, the Great Blue Ox. Oh, yes, there was Jim, his pet crow, also, but Jim could hardly be called an asset as he was usually getting into mischief.

There are a few rumors about Paul's courtship which may give an idea as to what a good match for him Mrs. Paul really was. Paul, having grown to young manhood in the far backwoods, had never had much of a chance for paying attention to the ladies, and accordingly he was somewhat bashful. One day, however, while out on one of his long rambles, he heard a woman's scream for help and, looking around, he saw a tall, handsome and very much excited girl rushing toward him at full tilt. "My sister has fallen in the river!" she cried to him. "Come and help me get her out before she drowns!" and turning back the way she had come, she dashed on ahead with Paul following.

He had to bestir himself to keep up with her, which in itself was so unusual that he immediately began to feel interested and forgot all about being bashful. When they arrived at the river bank, he looked far down to where the swollen waters of the big stream were rolling fast and deep, but not a sign of the sister could he see.

"She fell in ten miles upstream," the girl told him despairingly. "I ran down this far, hoping to be able to get down to the river and catch her when the current brings her by, but the banks are so high and steep all the way that I couldn't get near the water."

Paul didn't say a word but began working his very fastest, picking up great stones and logs and anything he could lay his hands on and throwing them down into the river bed. It wasn't more than a second or two before the girl caught onto his idea and began doing the same thing, and he was surprised to see that she heaved over almost as much rubble as he himself did. So, between the two of them, it wasn't very long—five or ten minutes perhaps—before they had dammed the river up tight, stopped the current and raised the water until they were able to reach right out and grab the sister when she floated into sight.

Of course the girl was grateful to Paul for saving her sister's life, and he thought a lot of her after seeing how quickly she caught onto his idea and how fast and well she could work. It was a match from the very start, and before very long they were married and as happy and contented as two bugs in a rug.

Mrs. Paul was about of a size to match her husband. It took forty-seven grizzly bear skins to make her a fur coat—that is, one of these short ones—and one of her skirts used up more canvas than a full-rigged ship. She was affectionate and lovable, and everyone said that Paul was mighty lucky to get such a wife. The only difference between her and other women was that of size—with her the measurements were yards or rods instead of inches.

As for Babe, the Great Blue Ox, just where Paul got him has never been learned. It is thought that he secured him when but a calf, being attracted by his strange blue color, and reared him from calfhood with great care. The Ox well repaid the kindness of his master, for he was with him through all his logging operations and was continually performing labors that could not have been done in any other way. The Great Blue Ox was so strong that he could pull anything that had two ends and some things that had no ends at all, which made him very valuable at times, as one can easily understand.

Babe was remarkable in a number of ways besides that of his color, which was a bright blue. His size is rather a matter of doubt, some people holding that he was twenty-four ax-handles and a plug of tobacco wide between the eyes, and others saying that he was forty-two ax-handles across the forehead. It may be that both are wrong, for the story goes that Jim, the pet crow, who always roosted on Babe's left horn, one day decided to fly across to the tip of the other horn. He got lost on the way and didn't get to the other horn until after the spring thaw, and he had started in the dead of winter.

The Great Blue Ox was so long in the body that an ordinary person, standing at his head, would have had to use a pair of field glasses in order to see what the animal was doing with his hind feet.

Babe had a great love for Paul, and a peculiar way of showing it which discovered the great logger's only weakness. Paul was ticklish, especially around the neck, and the Ox had a strong passion for licking him there with his tongue. His master good-naturedly avoided such outbursts of affection from his pet whenever possible.

So here was Paul Bunyan at last, no longer just a husky youngster but a man full grown and with a wife to care for. He was ready to embark upon his life's work and, having a pretty definite idea of what he wished to do, he decided to return to the part of the country where he had been born. More people were living along the coast and moving steadily inland, sawmills were being built to supply the growing demand for lumber, and woodsmen were making greater and greater encroachments upon the ancient and far-reaching forests to provide the logs that were needed in ever-increasing quantities.

Paul, foreseeing that with his great strength and his unequaled knowledge of the woods he would have little trouble in getting plenty of chances to show what he could do, packed his tools and other belongings, said good-by to his parents, and —with his wife comfortably riding along on the broad back of Babe—set out for the town of his origin.

IV

Paul Bunyan's Return

So here Paul came, once more nearing the town where he had been born. A giant figure of a fellow now, he pushed his way through the thick timber, bending aside the trees in his road as if they were stalks of grass. Following closely at his heels was Babe, with Mrs. Paul perched on his back, and Jim, the pet crow, comfortably riding on his left horn. They finally came out of the woods into a clearing, and there Paul decided to camp.

It so happened that a hunter stepped into the opposite side of the clearing just about the time that Paul and his companions appeared from among the trees. Unnoticed by the newcomers, he stood for a moment, gazing spellbound at what he saw. Then, with all haste that he could muster, he sneaked back along the path that he had come and ran with all speed towards town.

Breathlessly he burst upon the crowd of loafers before old Deacon White's store and told what he had seen. "I tell you I saw it myself," he shouted angrily as his listeners laughed in disbelief. "There he was, a great tall man that would make ten of any of you—yes, more than ten! Brushed the trees out of his way like grass, he did, and he had an ox with him that's as big as any forty oxen around these parts. A *blue* ox, at that, as blue as indigo! And if you don't believe me, you can go look for yourselves," with which defiance he stared around at his listeners in a high and mighty manner, proud of being the center of interest.

Deacon White, a very old man who was certainly the richest and shrewdest person in all the country around, had listened with interest to the hunter's story. "Um-m, well," he offered, "mebbe it's Paul Bunyan come home again. I don't calc'late it could be anyone else."

"And furthermore," he went on, glancing with contempt at the men before him, "if that's who it is, mebbe I can get him to log off that deestrict of mine back in the hills that none of you timid woodsmen will touch." With a snort of derision he turned his back on them and gave orders for his chore boy to saddle his horse at once. As soon as

[42]

he was mounted, he lost no time in galloping toward the clearing where the stranger was reported to be.

"Hallo, there," piped the Deacon, when he was finally in sight of the camp. "Be you Paul Bunyan?"

"That's my name!" Paul answered, bending low over the old man so that he could hear him better. He was very much pleased that some one remembered him after all the years he had been away.

"I thought so," explained the other. "I'm Deacon White. Lived in these parts a long time, I have. Knew your pappy and mammy, and knew you when you were a baby. He-he!" and the old man's white whiskers shook as he chuckled over certain memories. "You raised quite a ruckus around here then—don't reckon I'll ever forget all the excitement you stirred up," and the old man chuckled again.

Paul's gratification was beginning to turn to embarrassment when his visitor finally made his errand known.

"You showed so much promise as a youngster," said the Deacon, "that now I've come to offer you a good job of hard work that no one else is man enough to tackle."

"Bully for you!" responded Paul heartily. "That's just what I'm looking for. What is it?" Prospects of a difficult task interested him at once, for along with the great strength that Nature had given him, he had developed a passion for using that strength in the hardest kind of labor. It seemed a privilege for him to be able to do the grand and thrilling work of the woods. In fact, during his years as lumberman, whenever he found his men soldiering or loafing on the job—as sometimes happened once or twice a season when cabin fever infected them —he would send them all back to camp to think over their shame and joyfully do all their tasks by himself. So now he listened to what the Deacon had to offer. "If it has to do with the woods, and if it's worth while, I'm your man," he promised.

"It's all of that," the old man told him. "Back in the mountains I have several thousand sections of fine timber that has never been touched by an ax. I need these logs for my mills, but I can't get any of these half-portion lumbermen around here to log off the tract for me. It's said that there are a lot of Agropelters and Gumberoos there, and mebbe other critters as well, and they have scared every one else out so that they are afraid to go into those woods. I don't calc'late they could run you out, though, could they?" and he peered up at the giant form before him with such an amusing, quizzical look that Paul burst into a roar of laughter so loud that the old Deacon was thrown from his horse and the people back in town thought it was thundering.

Now Gumberoos and Agropelters were, in the early days, a very real danger to woodsmen, and any tract of timberland that sheltered them was rightly shunned by all ordinary persons. Most people today have never heard of them, having forgotten that long years ago, before most of the forests were cut down, there were a lot of queer animals living in the wild places where men seldom ventured. Most of these animals are now extinct because the lumbermen have destroyed their hiding places, but in the early days they were to be found here and there and some of them were very dangerous to man. There were the Ring-Tailed Bavalorous and the Whintosser, for instance, the Agropelter and the Gumberoo, the Snoligoster and a lot of others. At one time and another, as history shows, Paul Bunyan met up with quite a few of them during his logging operations.

The Agropelter was a very strange animal, and greatly feared because he had a special hatred for all mankind. No woodsman was ever anxious to run across him. He was very strong, with a slender, wiry body, a villainous ape-like face, and long thin arms like muscular whiplashes, so powerful that they could break off dead branches and hurl them with the force of a cannon ball. He liked to tuck himself away in the hollow of a dead and rotted tree and there lie in wait for his enemy, man, to come by. When a luckless human being happened to pass beneath his den, the Agropelter would seize a large club which he kept handy for the purpose, and with his whip-like arms would hurl it with such unerring aim that very seldom did he fail to crack the skull of the unlucky intruder.[1] The animal fed only upon hoot owls and woodpeckers, and the toughness of his diet, together with its scarcity, is thought to have been the cause of his continuous rage.

The Gumberoo was another fearsome creature that infested various stretches of woodland. He was almost round in shape, and was the largest animal in the woods. He was safe from all enemies because of his skin, which was like leather and so thick nothing could pierce it. He could eat a horse at one meal, and has been known to destroy a whole herd of moose without the least injury from the terrible horns of the fierce bulls. In fact, no creature was ever able to find a vulnerable spot in the animal's anatomy, for whatever struck the beast bounced off again with the same force. Even when a rifle was fired at him, so tough was his

[1] Only one man has ever been known to survive an attack by this fierce creature, and it is from him that the description of the animal has come. He was cruising timber near the St. Croix River when he encountered the beast, and luckily the club hurled at him was punky and soft from rot, so that it shattered against his head and barely stunned him for a moment. He opened his eyes again in time to see the rascally Agropelter slip away into the woods, and was able to observe it closely.

hide and so elastic his body, that the bullet was
sure to bounce back at exactly the same speed and
strike the hunter squarely between the eyes. He
was always hungry, always ready to eat anything
that looked like food, and was especially fond of
human beings.

There was one thing, however, which the Gumberoo greatly feared and which he had no protection against, and that was fire. He was of a very
inflammable nature, burning like celluloid if fire
ever touched him and finally blowing up with the
tremendous force of giant powder. Woodsmen
claim that occasionally the creatures could be
heard exploding with loud reports when they happened to get caught in forest fires, and it is thought
that the increasing prevalence of such fires has had
much to do with their scarcity of recent years. So
fearful of fire were they that just the smell of
smoke would drive them far away, and it was
through knowledge of this weakness that Paul and
his men eventually cleared the Deacon's woods of
these fierce creatures.[1]

[1] *Dermelasticus explodens* is the scientific name of the Gumberoo. It is believed to be totally extinct at the present time,
though occasionally during forest fires woodsmen will insist that
they hear explosions and can detect the odor of burning rubber
which they claim are sure signs that another Gumberoo has just
met his well-deserved fate. However, there is no authentic proof
that the animal has been seen in recent years.

So it was not very strange that the Deacon could find no one willing to log off timberlands where Agropelters and Gumberoos were lying in wait. Paul Bunyan, however, was quite different from other men, and he just laughed at the danger. "I'm your man, Deacon," he promised, and they at once began discussing terms. When they had come to an agreement, Paul said, "You draw up the papers, Deacon, and arrange for the necessary supplies of grub and tools and other things. I'll strike out for the woods at once, pick a location for my camp, and start getting my crew together. It'll soon be late fall now, and I want to start cutting by the time the first snow comes. Are there any men in town that I might have use for?"

The old man snorted in disgust. "All pretty poor stuff, except Swedish Ole, the blacksmith," he replied. "He's the biggest man around here, though not so big as you. When he puts shoes on a horse he takes the animal up on his lap like a baby. He's a mighty good blacksmith, all right, but I expect folks will be glad to get him out of town, as he's kind of clumsy, and they're all afraid of getting stepped on some time."

"I'll need a smith, and he sounds like a good man," said Paul. "You sign him up for me, and he can join me later. Meanwhile, I'll get busy as I have said and will manage to see you again before long," and after making further arrangements for his wife to accompany the Deacon back to town, where she was to remain while he was in the woods, Paul started away, followed by Babe, the Great Blue Ox.

He traveled many miles through the forest and over mountains and figured that he must be getting near the Deacon's tract of woodland. Then all at once he began to hear sounds like long peals of nearby thunder. He looked at the sky and saw that the sun was setting perfectly clear, with not a cloud to be seen, so he knew there could be no storm coming up. As he went on the sounds grew louder, and Paul became more puzzled then ever. Finally he came out into a cleared space on the side of a mountain where a forest fire had swept the slope clean of trees from bottom to top, and there he saw a very strange thing.

Hearing the thundering noise again, he looked ahead and was surprised to see a great round stone as big as a house rolling down the mountainside towards the valley below. It came bounding along at great speed, gaining momentum with every turn, and as it rolled along it jarred the earth with the thunderous sounds he had been hearing. But strangest of all was the man who was running along beside it, holding something tightly against it as it turned over and over. Paul looked more

[49]

closely, and saw other stones rolling down hill in the same manner, and along with each one, keeping pace with it, was a tall, strongly built man with something in his hand. "I wonder what queer new game they are playing," Paul said to himself, walking on to get a nearer view.

Then it was that he began to understand what the men were doing. Each of them had an ax in his hand, and was holding its edge to the stone as it turned over and over in its headlong flight down the steep slope. The men were grinding their axes!

Thus it was that Paul Bunyan caught first sight of the Seven Axmen, mighty men of the woods, whose heroic fame through later years was almost as great as his own. They were with him through most of his lumbering operations, and for many years they continued to sharpen their axes in this way, starting a huge round stone rolling down a long steep hill and running along beside it holding the edge of an ax to it as it turned. Later, when they moved with Paul to the Dakotas they found no hills steep or long enough to serve their purpose, and it was then that Paul invented the revolving grindstone so common today to take the place of the rolling rocks. But that was a later development.

The Seven Axmen! Noble figures they were,

never equaled before or since, excepting by Paul Bunyan himself. They were cousins, it is said, and came originally from Canada. Each could cut down several square miles of timber in a day without exerting himself and then not be too tired afterwards to join in the pranks and horseplay of the camp. They were jolly fellows, and Paul got along with them first-rate through many years.

Observing that they had company, the Axmen dropped their labors and came forward to greet the newcomer, all happy at having a visitor. They were congenial lads, with hearts as big as their two fists, and they welcomed Paul with great friendliness. They cast many admiring glances at his great size and at the hugeness of Babe, the Blue Ox, as one can well imagine, though they were almost as big as Paul themselves. With the greatest hospitality, they invited him to stay overnight with them, and so, just as the sun had set, they all presently came to the big log shanty where the Seven Axmen lived.

After their tools had been put away, their visitor accompanied them to the little lake nearby where they proceeded to wash up before supper, and such a splashing did the lot of them make that they splashed all the water out of the lake so that it was never of any use after that. Just then the supper horn blew, and they tramped back and into the shanty.

There Paul met the Little Chore Boy, a youngster who did the cooking, attended to the chores, and did all the light work that had to be done, while the Seven Axmen attended to all the heavy labor. As the Little Chore Boy weighed only eight hundred pounds, he had to put up with a great deal of joshing and teasing from the Seven Axmen because of his small size.

They all sat down to supper except the Little Chore Boy, whose duty it was to wait on them and who never sat down to table with full-grown men. Such a supper as it was! The Little Chore Boy was continually groaning under the weight of the food he carried to the table. The Seven Axmen were hearty eaters—a half of a full-grown hog was only a slice of bacon to them—and Paul's appetite was so much greater even than theirs that he immediately won the deep admiration of them all.

Finally the toothpicks were passed, and everybody sat back and began to fill his pipe. Paul had been wondering what the cord of firewood was on the table for, until he found out that the Seven Axmen used cordwood for toothpicks. When all had their pipes going, they moved away from the table to give the Little Chore Boy a chance to clean up.

Babe often showed his affection for Paul with a loving, juicy lick of his great tongue

Paul had never found anyone he liked so well as he did these Seven Axmen. He could see that they were all good lumbermen, too, well acquainted with the work of logging off timber and accustomed to doing everything in a big way, and so he started in telling them about the contract he had made to log the Deacon's tract.

They were greatly interested, nor did they hesitate in giving him an answer when he offered them top places on his crew. They liked hard work —the harder the job the better they liked it— and to work for such a mighty man as Paul Bunyan appealed to them very strongly. They accepted his offer, there and then.

Afterwards, everybody being greatly pleased over the new arrangements, they lounged before the fire and sang *Bung Yer Eye* and *Shanty Boy* until the people back along the coast miles away thought a storm was blowing up.

V

Paul's Camp
in Maine

Paul's first task, after he and the Seven Axmen had finally come to the place in the Deacon's woods where he intended to build his camp,
was to get rid of the Gumberoos and Agropelters.
So while the Axmen all seated themselves, leaned
their backs comfortably against broad tree trunks
and lit their pipes, Paul stood thinking out some
method of driving the troublesome creatures
away. Paul was a great thinker, and there was
never any problem that could keep him puzzled
long.

"The Gumberoos are afraid of fire," he said to
himself, "and they will run away if they notice
even the least sign of it. Now that is a weakness
that I ought to be able to use against them—but
how?" and he thought so hard over the matter

that the Seven Axmen could hear the low whir of his brain working. Just then a big cloud of smoke from one of the Axmen's pipes floated up and encircled Paul's head, and when he finally stopped coughing and had caught his breath again a look of great satisfaction spread over his face. He had figured out a way to drive the Gumberoos away.

"I want you bullies to rest up for a few days," he said to the Seven Axmen, and there was a twinkle in his eyes. "There's plenty of hard work on the job ahead, but I'm not quite ready for you to start on it yet. So just you sit around and take things easy for a while, until I am ready for you to begin," and he tossed down his big tobacco pouch where all could reach it and sauntered away.

The Seven Axmen looked at one another and grinned, and then they proceeded to fill up their pipes again. If their new boss wanted to pay them their wages just for loafing, why, they were perfectly willing to accommodate him. They had often looked forward to such a time as this, when they might take their ease and talk and smoke together, all without being worried by the thought that they were leaving necessary tasks undone or were losing valuable working time. Never before had the opportunity of indulging in such fancied leisure come to them, and now they settled back to enjoy themselves to the fullest extent.

Many were the subjects which they discussed and great the problems which they settled. Countless were the tales of woodland adventure which they told, and mighty were the labors each performed in the telling. Oh, wonderful men, those Seven Axmen—wonderful in brain as well as in muscle. So tireless were their minds that they could listen to the same joke a hundred times a day and laugh each time harder than the last.

And all the time while they rested they smoked their pipes, wonderful old pipes which they had used constantly through many, many years. Each one used up two bushels of tobacco every time it was filled, and by the time the second day had come to an end the contents of Paul's tobacco pouch were almost half gone. The smoke hung over the land like a cloud, and for hundreds of miles there was not a Gumberoo to be found in the woods.

The fierce creatures, sniffing the strangling smoke which filled the air, had been fooled into thinking that a terrible fire was raging through the forest. Frightened nearly out of their wits, they had scrambled away as fast as they could roll. No one knows how far they went ere their flight ceased, for they were never seen nor heard of again in that part of the country.

Getting rid of the Agropelters was the next task, and this required a little more work. Paul called the Seven Axmen to him, and they were very glad to put away their pipes and gather around him. They had smoked so much that their tongues were sore, and their two-day rest had grown so tiresome that they were anxious to get back to hard work again. "These Agropelters all hide away in the hollows of dead trees," Paul told them. "Now I want you to get your axes and wander through the timber. Every time you see a dead tree, or one with a hollow in it, chop it down and split it open. After you have done that, we'll start putting up the camp."

With a whoop, the Seven Axmen set about the task as if it were a great game. Being so large and strong, they had no fear of the animals, and as one blow from their great axes was usually enough to smash even the biggest hollow tree into splinters, they worked very fast. It was only a day or so before there was not a hollow tree to be found standing in all the Deacon's timberland, and with their hiding places all gone, the Agropelters also fled far away.

Paul was very much pleased that the woods were now safe for ordinary men, and he praised the Seven Axmen highly for their work. He set them to putting up bunkhouses and stables and the cook shanty for the new camp, and he ordered the Little Chore Boy to carry the word far and near that now, since the dangerous animals were all driven out of the woods, he would be giving high pay that winter to all good loggers who cared to join his crew.

Men soon began drifting into camp from every direction, and Paul hired all the best ones. A man had to be extra good to get a job with Paul Bunyan, but even so it wasn't so very long before he had gathered together as sturdy a bunch of woodsmen as has ever been seen.

It was along about this time that he made a trip back to town, where he saw the Deacon again and arranged all the little matters that were so far unsettled regarding the work, and when he started on his return trip to camp he was accompanied by Ole, the smith. Ole, or the Big Swede, as he was quite often called, was a slow-witted but amiable chap whose mind could never hold more than one idea at a time. He was gigantic in size— though not as big as Paul—and was a past-master in all that had to do with his trade of metal-working. From the first, he regarded Paul with a liking that was almost worship, and next to Paul in his affections came Babe, the Great Blue Ox. Indeed, so remarkable was his admiration for the magnificent animal that Paul at once turned over to him the duty of caring for Babe, which task he gladly accepted and continued to perform through many years. When finally his work as smith began to demand all of his time, he reluctantly turned Babe over to the gentle ministrations of Brimstone Bill, but that did not happen until a long while later.

Paul had taken the Blue Ox with him to town, and there he loaded him with all the supplies that would be needed for the camp and crew during the winter. When everything had been packed on Babe's back, the animal was so heavily laden that on the way back to camp he sank to his knees in the solid rock at nearly every step. These footprints later filled with water and became the countless lakes which are to be found today scattered throughout the state of Maine.

Babe was compelled to go slowly, of course, on account of the great load he carried, and so Paul had to camp overnight along the way. He took the packs from the Ox's back, turned the big animal out to graze, and after eating supper he and Ole lay down to sleep.

The Blue Ox, however, was for some strange reason in a restless mood that night, and after feeding all that he cared to, he wandered away for many miles before he finally found a place that suited his particular idea of what a bedding ground should be. There he lay down, and it is quite possible that he was very much amused in thinking of the trouble which his master would have in finding him the next morning. The Ox was a very wise creature, and every now and then he liked to play a little joke on Paul.

Along about dawn Paul Bunyan awoke and looked about for his pet. Not a glimpse of him could he get in any direction, though he whistled so loudly for him that the nearby trees were shattered into bits. At last, after he and Ole had eaten their breakfast and Babe still did not appear, Paul knew that the joke was on him. "He thinks he has put up a little trick on me," he said to Ole with a grin. "You go ahead and make up the packs again, while I play hide-and-seek for a while," and as the Big Swede started gathering everything together again he set off trailing the missing animal.

Babe's tracks were so large that it took three men, standing close together, to see across one of them, and they were so far apart that no one could follow them but Paul, who was an expert trailer, no one else ever being able to equal him in this ability. So remarkable was he in this respect that he could follow any tracks that were ever made, no matter how old or how faint they were. It is told of him that he once came across the carcass of a bull moose that had died of old age, and having a couple of hours to spare, and being also of an inquiring turn of mind, he followed the tracks of the moose back to the place where it had been born.

Being such an expert, therefore, it did not take him very long to locate Babe. The Great Blue Ox, when he at last came across him, was lying down contentedly chewing his cud, and waiting for his master to come and find him. "You worthless critter!" Paul said to him, and thwacked him good-naturedly with his hand. "Look at the trouble you have put me to, and just look at the damage you have done here," and he pointed to the great hollow place in the ground which Babe had wallowed out while lying there. The Ox's only reply was to smother Paul for a moment with a loving, juicy lick of his great tongue, and then together they set off to where Ole was waiting for them.

Anyone, by looking at a map of the state of Maine, can easily locate Moosehead Lake, which is, as history shows, the place where the Great Blue Ox lay down.

By the time that Paul, Ole and Babe arrived at the logging camp, the first snow had begun to fall, and Paul began to work in earnest. He organized his crew so that each gang of men had a certain task to do, and the rules he developed here and used in his later logging operations have been followed more or less in all lumber camps ever since.

For instance, in the Great Lakes states, where the lumber industry probably reached its highest development, the work of the average logging crew was done much in this way: A gang of choppers would first go through the woods clearing the way. After them would come the sawyers, one man carrying an ax for marking the direction of each tree's fall and a wedge to use if necessary in guiding it, while two others would fell the tree with a crosscut saw. (Paul was the inventor of the two-man saw used in logging, and Ole made up a number from his plans for use in his camps.) The saw having done its work, as the tree began to topple the sawyers would get back out of the way, giving a loud yell, "Timber-r!" as a warning to anyone else nearby, and the great trunk would come swishing and crashing to the ground.

Then would come the scaler, who would measure the fallen trees into the proper log lengths, and the sawyers would cut them at his marks. Next, the skidding crew or swampers would clear the way for the teamsters, who would drag or haul the logs to the stagings by the stream. Winter was always best for logging, for then the logs could be easily skidded over the icy roads which had been made slippery by sprinkling water on them until they were paved with hard and solid ice.

At the stream the deckers would pile the logs on the skidways, from which, in the spring when the freshets filled the stream with swift water, they would be dumped to float down-river on the big drive. When the time of the drive came, the entire crew would join in following it, riding the logs with calked boots and carrying pike pole or peavy, fighting jams and snaking stranded logs off the banks all along the way. When the logs finally reached the booms of the sawmill toward which they were headed, the logger's work was over, and he usually celebrated the ending of the drive in a grand and glorious manner, fighting out old grudges accumulated during the winter and otherwise enjoying himself.

That is something of the way a logging crew usually works. Of course, Paul had the help of the remarkable Babe and of such mighty woodsmen as the Seven Axmen, and he did things in his own peculiar way which no one else could hope to imitate. In the main, however, the camps of later years were organized much after the fashion that he established.

No one, certainly, could be expected to copy him in the matter of straightening out crooked logging trails. It was all wild country where Paul did his logging, and about the only roads which he found through the woods were the trails and paths made by the wild animals that had traveled over them for hundreds of years. Paul decided to use these game trails as logging roads, but they twisted and turned in every direction and were all so crooked that they had to be straightened before any use could be made of them. It is well known that the Great Blue Ox was so powerful that he could pull anything that had two ends, and so when Paul wanted a crooked logging trail straightened out, he would just hitch Babe up to one end of it, tell his pet to go ahead, and, lo and behold! the crooked trail would be pulled out perfectly straight.

There was one particularly bad stretch of road, about twenty or thirty miles long, that gave Babe and Paul a lot of trouble before they finally got all the crooks pulled out of it. It certainly must have been the crookedest road in the world—it twisted and turned so much that it spelled out every letter of the alphabet, some of the letters two or three times. Paul taught Babe how to read just by leading him over it a few times, and men going along it met themselves coming from the other direction so often that the whole camp was near crazy before long.

So Paul decided that the road would have to be

straightened out without any further delay, and with that end in view he ordered Ole to make for him the strongest chain he knew how. The Big Swede set to work with a will, and when the chain was completed it had links four feet long and two feet across and the steel they were made of was thirteen inches thick.

The chain being ready, Paul hitched Babe up to one end of the road with it. At his master's word the Great Blue Ox began to puff and pull and strain away as he had never done before, and at last he got the end pulled out a little ways. Paul chirped to him again, and he pulled away harder than ever. With every tug he made one of the twists in the road would straighten out, and then Babe would pull away again, hind legs straight out behind and belly to the ground. It was the hardest job Babe had ever been put up against, but he stuck to it most admirably.

When the task was finally done, the Ox was nearly fagged out, a condition that he had never known before, and that big chain had been pulled on so hard that it was pulled out into a solid steel bar. The road was straightened out, however, which was the thing Paul wanted, and he considered the time and energy expended as well worth while, since the nuisance had been transformed into something useful. He found, though, that since all the kinks and twists had been pulled out, there was now a whole lot more of the road than was needed, but—never being a person who could stand to waste anything which might be useful—he rolled up all the extra length and laid it down in a place where there had never been a road before but where one might come in handy some time.

Nor was the straightening of crooked roads the only useful work which the Great Blue Ox did. It was also his task to skid or drag the logs from the stumps to the rollways by the streams, where they were stored for the drives. Babe was always obedient, and a tireless and patient worker. It is said that the timber of nineteen states, except a few scant sections here and there which Paul Bunyan did not touch, was skidded from the stumps by the all-powerful Great Blue Ox. He was docile and willing and could be depended upon for the performance of almost any task set him, except that once in a while he would develop a sudden streak of mischief and drink a river dry behind a drive or run off into the woods. Sometimes he would step on a ridge that formed the bank of the river and smash it down so that the river would start running out through his tracks, thus changing its course entirely from what Paul had counted on.

The cutting of the Deacon's timber tract went

[69]

ahead so fast that Paul began looking ahead and wondering what he would do next. He was very much gratified to find that his fame had already begun to spread, so that he was offered enough logging contracts to keep him busy in that section of the country for several years to come. He was never one to shirk a task, was Paul, and the assurance of having ahead of him all the work that he could do made him happy indeed.

VI

The Little Blue Ox

I<small>N</small> addition to the stories of his great logging
feats in Maine, there are also several interesting things told about Paul Bunyan at this time
which are conducive to a clearer understanding of
his exceptional powers and show his remarkable
ability for doing big things in a big way. For instance, he could ride logs through water which
ran so fast that it would tear in two any ordinary
man who might try to drink of it. It is said of him
also that he was the greatest log-roller that ever
wore calked boots.

A favorite lumberjack sport is rolling a log. A
man stands on a big log afloat in the water and
starts turning it with his feet, keeping his feet
going so that he is always on top and standing
safely upright, no matter how fast he gets the log
to whirling under him. Paul Bunyan could roll a
log so fast that it made foam on the water solid
enough for him to walk ashore on, and he is known

to have crossed wide rivers in this way. Not all of this foam which he thus caused has disappeared to this day, and occasionally small bits of it may still be seen floating down many streams after a heavy rain.

As a white-water man, though, probably the greatest and hardest task which Paul ever had was when he poled a big raft of logs upstream over Niagara Falls. He came very near losing out several times on that adventure, but he stuck to it as only he could do and eventually succeeded, as usual, in finishing what he had started. He was nearly fagged out, however, for a few minutes afterwards.

Along with his hard work, the great logger enjoyed a little sport now and then. Best of all, he liked to hunt, and no one has ever equaled him as a hunter. He had a rifle that would kill game farther away than the average man could travel in a week, and he had invented a shotgun so powerful that it would kill wild geese so high in the air they would spoil before they could fall to the ground. He had a great deal of trouble that way until he hit on the idea of putting salt on his shot, which preserved the birds as they fell and allowed them to get to the ground while they were still fit for food.

Once, when Paul was out hunting, he spotted a deer five miles or so away, sticking its head over a fallen tree, and taking careful aim with his trusty rifle, he fired at it. The deer disappeared, but to his great surprise, a second later it again stuck its head into view. "My aim must be getting poor," grumbled Paul as he rubbed his eyes, and then he let drive at the animal again. To his even greater astonishment, the deer's head had no more than dropped out of sight from his second shot than it lifted up in the same place again. The exasperated hunter kept on firing, and each time the strange performance was repeated the deer bobbed up into view again after each shot. He had only twenty-eight cartridges, and he fired them all. It was not until he had used his last one that the deer's head went down and stayed out of sight.

"Well, I got him at last, but that was certainly poor shooting," Paul muttered sadly to himself as he walked ahead to pick up the carcass of the animal. He was feeling very badly over his poor marksmanship, as was quite natural, since he was always before able to hit whatever he aimed at, no matter how poor the shooting conditions were. One can imagine how surprised he was, and how reassured, when he looked behind the fallen tree and found twenty-eight dead deer there, every one with a bullet hole exactly between the eyes. The whole herd had taken turns at peeping over the deadfall, and Paul had thought that it was the same animal reappearing each time. When he got back to camp, he sent the Little Chore Boy out to bring in the game—which he was able to do in one load—and that evening for supper the crew enjoyed a feast of fresh venison. The remarkable thing about the whole proceeding is that the number of cartridges which Paul had with him should have so exactly coincided with the number of deer in the herd.

It was while Paul Bunyan was logging in Maine that he secured Willie, the Little Blue Ox, from a farmer. The great logger happened by chance to see the calf, and he was at once greatly attracted to him because the young animal was exactly the color of Babe. He quickly hunted up the farmer and asked him what price he wanted for the blue calf.

"Sell him?" exclaimed the farmer. "Why, I'll be more than glad to give him away. He's a great eater, that calf is. He eats down forty acres of hay in a day, since he was weaned four days ago, and then doesn't have enough. My farm is only a section, and as only a quarter of it is in hay I have been able to feed him for only four days. If I keep him over until to-morrow I'll have to buy a new farm, so if you want him, stranger, just take him along, and I won't charge you a cent."

Paul was delighted and at once got the calf out

of the pasture, put a rope around his neck and started leading him back to camp. The poor calf was underfed when his new master got him, but he soon recovered. As it happened, Paul had long ago taught Babe to eat pine branches or needles, or any other green stuff that could be found plentifully in the woods, and just as soon as he got Willie he set about teaching the young animal to acquire the same taste. The Little Blue Ox was so hungry that he learned almost instantly, and Paul walked very slowly on the way back to camp, allowing the calf to browse along as they traveled. The animal kept eating so fast and so much as he went along that every time his new master looked back, Willie had grown two feet taller. When they got to camp, the Little Blue Ox was put into a specially built barn, with a great mass of pine branches in the manger to keep him contented. During the night, however, the calf continued to grow, and the next morning he was found several miles away, grazing about with the barn perched on his back.

Paul had great expectations for Willie, intending to yoke him up with Babe when he should get his full growth. The Little Blue Ox was quite a disappointment, though, and he was never of much service on account of his great love for flapjacks. He was never willing to work any distance away from the cook shanty, and every chance he got he would spend his time standing with his head through one of the shanty windows and bothering the cooks to distraction, ready to gobble up any stray flapjack that might wander by. His master was never able to cure him of this strange passion, and it was ultimately the cause of his sad death later on.

Through several years—it is not known exactly how many—Paul Bunyan continued his logging operations in Maine, establishing camps here and there as his work was done in different districts. He was always inventing and trying out new tools, and he finally had Ole, the smith, make for him a great crosscut saw with a blade long enough to reach three miles.

Paul was very eager to try out his new invention, for he hoped that it would cut down trees faster than all his other tools together. When he tried using it, however, he found it unsatisfactory. Maine is a very mountainous state, as every one knows, with hills almost everywhere, and when Paul tried using his big saw there he found that it would only cut the timber on the tops of the hills, leaving that in the valleys untouched. Most of the best timber had been cut in Maine, anyway, and so he began to long for a change of scene— some new level land where the trees grew big and close together, and where he would have ample opportunity for giving a fair test to his latest invention.

It was about this time that certain things occurred which gave him the chance to carry out his ambition. The King of Sweden had just driven all the good farmers out of that country, and a Senator from North Dakota wanted all the fine upstanding timber cleared off the whole state—and probably off of South Dakota as well—so as to make room for the Swedish farmers and attract them there with rich, free, ready-cleared farmland. He had heard of Paul Bunyan's great work in Maine, and so he asked him to do the job. Paul accepted the contract, and that is how he came to log off the Dakotas, doing the job all in one winter and causing those states to become the great treeless plains which they now are.

"Swedish Ole, the blacksmith, is the biggest man around here. When he puts shoes on a horse he takes the animal up on his lap like a baby."

VII

Paul's Great
Flapjack Griddle

WHEN Paul Bunyan arrived in the Dakotas, he was very much pleased over the prospects there of being able to set up a new logging record. The timberlands of those states were ideal for his work, the easy conditions being quite different from the harsh ones he had known in Maine and the other eastern states. In the first place, most of the land was so level that it was very easy to get the logs to the streams, and the trails were already so straight that there was but little work for Babe to do in straightening them. In fact, this new location was just about all that could be desired for logging on a tremendous scale, and Paul set to work with great enthusiasm.

Paul had been accompanied westward by most of the men who had been with him in Maine.

There were the Seven Axmen, the Little Chore Boy and the faithful Ole, of course. Then, in addition, there were such famous loggers as Chris Crosshaul, Hard-jaw Murphy, Windy Night, Red-nose Jack and Blue-nose Mack, Shot Gunderson, Handy Hank, Brimstone Bill and a whole host of others, mighty workers every one of them, and all as proud as pouter pigeons to be working for such a boss as Paul Bunyan.

Both Babe and Willie, the Big and Little Blue Oxen, came along, too, following close on their master's heels all the way and carrying on their backs all the tools, supplies and other property that was to be used in the new camp. Some historians think that Paul also moved all of his camp buildings to the Dakotas, but that was probably done on one of his later moves, as the biggest building from his Maine camp would hardly have been big enough even for a tool house in his Red River Camp, after it got to going full blast.

Paul left his old camp in Maine very early in the morning, and so anxious was he to get located in his new camp that he hurried along at quite a fast pace, so that he arrived on the banks of what was afterwards called the Red River along about sunset of that afternoon. Most of his men kept up with him pretty well, but some of the stragglers didn't arrive until along some time the next morning.

Paul saw at once that he would be able to work very fast in clearing off this level land. "These pines must be a new variety," he said to the Big Swede. "I have never seen any quite like them before. Do you notice how none of them stand up straight, but all lean the same way? I think I'll give them the name of 'Leaning Pines,' and notify the tree experts back East so they can write about them in books." Indeed, there was something very peculiar about the big trees that covered the land so thickly, for they all leaned at just exactly the same angle toward the south.

Ole, however, shook his head over what Paul had said. "Ay tank they bane ordinary White Pines," he disagreed. "Ay tank Hugags make 'em lean that way." It so happened that this time Ole was more right than Paul, for the leaning trees were not a new species at all. Their strange peculiarity had been caused, as the Big Swede suspected, by the Hugag, a frightful looking but entirely harmless animal which was then to be found in great numbers in the Dakota woods.

The Hugag was quite large, with a body like a buffalo, and often weighed as much as two tons. Its head and neck were absolutely hairless, its wrinkled ears flopped downward, its bushy tail waggled constantly, and it had long muscular lips which prevented it from feeding on grass or other low-growing herbage but which were of the greatest use—like the trunk of an elephant—in stripping from trees the bark and twigs which were its usual food. Its greatest oddity, though, was its legs. They were long and stiff and perfectly straight, being entirely without joints in them, and since they therefore could not be bent the Hugag could never lie down as other animals do. It lived its whole life, waking and sleeping, upon its feet. Occasionally one would by some chance fall or be thrown to the ground, and as it could not bend its legs to get to its feet again, it was then perfectly helpless and soon died of fright or starvation.

Its strange manner of sleeping was the cause of the leaning pines. When it wanted to take a nap, it would face the west and lean its left side against the trunk of a pine tree, brace its hind legs firmly but never ceasing to mark time with its splay-footed front ones, hang down its head and close its eyes, and in this manner it would rest comfortably. Countless Hugags had followed these exact habits through many centuries, and the pressure of their weight against the trees of the Dakota woods had after many years caused all the pines to lean toward

[84]

the south in the manner which had at first deceived Paul.[1]

The uniform slant of the trees was a great aid in cutting them, for they all fell in exactly the same direction without any guidance on the part of the cutters. Paul was therefore able to use his great three-mile saw to the best advantage. When its blade passed through the forest, it ate its way through the thousands of trunks in its path like a mowing machine in a hay field and left the trees lying evenly side by side in windrows on the ground, ready to be cut into logs and snaked away.

Paul was so strong that he did not have to have much help with the big saw, and he usually put the Little Chore Boy on the other end to balance it down. He didn't care whether the Little Chore Boy did much saw work with the other end or not, and he never said anything when the youngster would hang onto the saw-handle and ride back and forth as the blade cut through the trees, but he did occasionally get a little angry when the lad

[1] The most successful hunters of this queer animal followed the custom of cutting partly through the bases of trees until they were almost ready to fall, so that when the Hugag leaned against one both the tree and animal would come down. As it could not then get to its feet again, it was easily captured or killed. Since the Hugag has almost entirely disappeared, this method of hunting has been abandoned and forgotten, as it has never proven successful with any other animal.

thoughtlessly allowed his feet to drag on the ground.

After the full crew got to working in the Dakota woods, the trees were cut down so fast that it was not very long before the poor Hugags could no longer find places to lean, and as a result they soon began perishing for lack of sleep. Nearly all of them died during the winter that Paul had his big camp on the Red River, and it is only very rarely that a stray one has been seen since that time.

It was on the banks of the Red River of the North that Paul had set up his camp, and there he assembled one of the greatest logging crews that has ever existed. So many men did he have in camp that one of his bunkhouses had a hundred and thirty-seven tiers of bunks, and the men used to go to bed with balloons and come down in the morning with parachutes. It was a pretty sight to see them early of a morning pouring out of their bunks and floating down in great clouds just about the time that the cooks were getting breakfast well under way.

No alarm clocks were needed in Paul's camp. He knew lumberjacks pretty well, Paul did, and so he just had a big pipe stretched from the cook shanty to the bunkhouses and a blower fixed in it. In the morning, when the cooks had their fires going, the victuals beginning to cook and the coffee simmering, the blower fan was turned on and the smell of breakfast blown right into the bunkhouses. Then, if a jack didn't grab his parachute and jump out of his bunk right away the camp doctor was sent to look him over, for everyone knew that he must be sick.

Paul found that feeding his many men was a good deal of a job, and especially did he find it hard to give them all the flapjacks they wanted, for they all seemed to have developed an extraordinary craving for this favorite delicacy. Since all of his men were so fond of flapjacks, he had to figure out some way to give them all they wanted, for he liked to keep his helpers satisfied.

The special flapjack stove which he had brought with him from Maine had disappeared in a very strange manner shortly after his arrival in the Dakotas. The queer passion for hot cakes which constantly stirred Willie, the Little Blue Ox, had grown rather than abated, and one morning he had stuck his head into the kitchen and eaten the day's supply at one gulp. He topped off this tidbit by swallowing the redhot flapjack stove as dessert, and as a result he developed a very painful case of stomach ache from which he soon died. Just what Paul did with his body is not certain, though the story goes that he sold the carcass that year (it was about 1857 when Willie died, it is said) to various packing companies in Chicago. These meat packers made a very good thing out of the remains of poor Willie, working him up and selling him for high prices.

Not all of their stock has been disposed of yet, so much of him was there, and thousands of people in this day and age are familiar with "canned Willie." It is rumored that most of him that was still on hand when the Great War broke out was sold to the government to feed the soldiers and sailors, and some day there may be an investigation to find out if this is true or not.

Paul Bunyan puzzled over the problem of getting enough flapjacks for his men, and finally he ordered Big Ole to make him a huge griddle. So big was this griddle that the cookees greased it with telephone poles on the ends of which were tied great bunches of gunny sacks for swabs. As Paul kept on hiring more men all the time, however, it was not very long before it became far too small, and he had his problem to settle all over again.

Some one at last told him where he could get a much bigger griddle to take the place of the one that was now outgrown, but it was so large that he couldn't at first figure out how to get it to camp. Luckily it was perfectly round in shape, and though it was so thick when it was stood on edge that it made a track as wide as a wagon road and was terribly hard to lift, Paul soon thought out a way to get it to the place where he wanted it.

Being so hard pressed by the need of more flapjacks in camp, he had started working the inventive side of his brain again, and it was at this time that he invented the electro magnet. He and Ole made two enormous big ones so strong that when they were tested out for the first time they pulled all the axes and saws and other tools out of the hands of the men in the woods within five miles of the camp. Seeing the trouble they had caused, Paul shut off the magnets at once, but it was worse than a jig-saw puzzle sorting out all the things that had been pulled into camp. He was quite pleased, however, with such a demonstration by the magnets, for he knew that they were just the things to help him get the big griddle to where he wanted it.

Shortly before this he had bought a team of mules, Jerry and Jinny, intending to use them occasionally while he gave Babe a rest. This Mule Team could travel so fast, after they had had their regular feed of ten bushels of wheat apiece, that no one else could hold them in, and so Paul always had to drive them himself. He used them hitched to a big flat-bottomed wagon without wheels.

So now he harnessed his mules up, fixed his new magnets in the back of the wagon, and drove off to where the griddle was. He swung the magnets around until their strength drew the griddle right up on its edge, and then he drove off lippity-cut towards the camp. The pull of the magnets got the griddle going around so fast and following him at such a great rate of speed that he hardly knew how to stop it, for the faster the mules went, just that much faster did the griddle roll along behind trying to catch up. It was clearly impossible for him to run away from it.

When he at last passed over the spot where he wanted it, he just dropped the magnets out of the wagon and pulled up to one side to watch what would happen. It rolled around and around, like a big piepan circling about on the floor as it loses its speed after some one spins it, getting nearer and nearer to where the magnets lay. It kept rolling weaker and weaker, until finally it twisted around a couple of times more just at the place where he wanted it and gouged out a big hole in the ground as it turned. Then it settled down, as nice as you please, right flat over the hole it had dug, and there it was at last, all ready for use and with a place for the fire underneath.

Paul then built a high fence around the griddle, and right beside it he put a couple of big buildings to hold his pancake flour. So perfectly did he have these buildings arranged that others just like them are used to-day as elevators for storing grain. He also invented a machine for mixing up the hot cake batter, and had Ole make eight or ten of them, which were placed in position by the griddle. These machines of Paul's are also copied to-day, and anyone may see many small models of them being used by paving contractors for mixing concrete.

"There now," said Paul to Sourdough Sam, the head baker of the camp, who also had charge of all the flapjack making, "there is a griddle to be proud of—a griddle which it should be a pleasure to work with. Everything is nice and handy, there is plenty of room to insure the best of results, and from now on you should find the subject of flapjacks as interesting as that of your sourdough bread."

Sam was doubtful at first, for he had had several disastrous experiments with flapjacks in the past—once having his mixing vat burst and flood the landscape for miles around with thin and sticky flapjack batter—and he was not at all optimistic about making hot cakes on the tremendous scale which Paul had just made provision for.

[91]

However, after he began to get used to the new arrangements, he began also to get interested in the intricacies of flapjack making. It was not long, therefore, until he was turning out his giant hot cakes with all the artistry which he had hitherto reserved exclusively for his first love, sourdough bread. From that time on his flapjacks were so wonderful that men still talk about them, and no other griddle expert has ever been able to equal him in the preparation of this supreme delicacy.

Everything was worked out on a very definite schedule, and it was truly a wonderful sight to see the big griddle being put to its daily use. Along in the afternoon every day a gang of three hundred flapjack cooks would start getting down the flour and fixin's from the elevators, start the mixers going and stir up the batter under the careful supervision of the boss baker. Meanwhile, as the batter was being mixed, the cook-boys would have to grease the griddle. This they did by strapping whole hams or sides of bacon on their feet and skating around over the hot surface. Paul had to have negroes for this task, as white men could not stand the heat.

When the batter was all ready and the greasing done, someone on the edge would blow a whistle, and so big was the griddle that it took four minutes for the sound to get across. At this signal,

PAUL'S GREAT FLAPJACK GRIDDLE

all the darkey cook-boys would skate to the edge
and climb high on the fence that had been fixed
for that purpose. A cook would then trip the
chute from the mixers, and out would roll a wave
of flapjack batter ten feet high. Any poor cook-
boy who hadn't climbed out of the way, and was
overtaken by the spreading batter, was in the
worst kind of luck, for he would be found later in
the flapjack just like a raisin in a cake.

Paul had a hard time at first figuring out how to
flip the flapjack over onto its other side so that
both sides of it would be cooked the same. Everyone has, of course, seen flapjacks flipped up in the
air out of a skillet, so that when they come down
again they have turned completely over and the
undone side has a chance to get browned in its
turn. Of course, the big griddle and the flapjack
on it were far too heavy for any wrist to flip in the
ordinary manner, and so for a while everybody had
to eat flapjack that was done only on one side. Paul
tried rigging a block-and-tackle arrangement for
turning the big hot cake over, but that did not
work very well, and the plan was abandoned.

At last he hit on the scheme of flipping it over
with dynamite, which plan worked out so well that
it was used from that time on. Whenever one side
of the flapjack became done, he would explode a
ton or so of dynamite under it, and away up in

[93]

the air the big cake would sail until it was almost out of sight. By putting a few more sticks under one side than under the other, he made sure that it would turn over while in the air, and so nicely did he calculate the exact amount of explosive to use each time that when the flapjack came down again it landed exactly on the griddle with the brown side uppermost.

After this, Paul's men never had any cause for kicking about the flapjacks in the Red River Camp, except occasionally when a cook-boy was caught by the batter and served up in the hot cake— which usually didn't happen more than two or three times a month.

VIII

The Red River Camp

THE great flapjack griddle was not the only noteworthy feature of Paul's Red River Camp, however, nor did his men dine exclusively upon flapjacks—as one might perhaps think they did from the attention given that particular item of the menu. Indeed, other foods made up most of every meal, the flapjacks being merely served for dessert, and the kitchen of the great cook shanty where most of the dishes were prepared was so big that the hundreds of cooks and all their helpers could work in it and never get in one another's way. Like everything else in any of Paul Bunyan's camps, the cooking was well organized, and each person in all the army of cooks, first and second assistant cooks, fire-tenders, pot-rustlers, butchers and dishwashers had his own particular work to do, and did it in the quickest and best way possible.

Even Ole, the Big Swede, had a place in the

kitchen—a regular forge, with anvil and all the special tools which he needed on the days when the cooks made up enough doughnuts to last the camp for the coming week. On Doughnut Days there he would stand over his anvil, bare-armed and streaming with sweat, catching the doughnuts as fast as the cooks could pass them to him, laying them on his anvil and punching the holes in them with almost a single motion.

In this and Paul's later camps there were a number of men who had jobs that are never heard of in ordinary camps to-day. For instance, there was a crew of eleven teamsters, with teams and scrapers, who were kept busy all the time just clearing away the coffee-grounds and eggshells from around the kitchen door. Another and much larger gang had almost more than they could do hauling away the tremendous heaps of prune seeds that accumulated after every meal and piling them on the roads. The prune seeds, after they were graded and packed down, made fine logging roads, as they only needed a little water sprinkled over them to make them slippery again, and then logs could be snaked over them with ease. Before the winter was over Paul had a very good prune seed highway stystem over most of North and South Dakota.

In addition to the coffee-ground and prune

seed crews, there were the men who drove the
salt and pepper wagons, going down the full
length of one of the big dinner tables in the dining
hall the first half of the week, filling the salt and
pepper shakers, and coming back the last half. The
teamster that drove the catsup wagon, though, always ran out of catsup before he got halfway
through with his trip, and so finally one day he
became disgusted with such a job and dumped his
wagon with its load into the river. The catsup
colored the water, which is red to this day, thus
giving to the stream the name of Red River which
it still bears.

Of all the camp tasks, however, probably the
lightest and easiest one was that of putting points
on the toothpicks, and the man who filled this job
considered himself quite lucky.

The mess hall in the Red River Camp was so
large that Paul had to have lunch counters along
the sides so that his men could stop and get something to eat while finding their places at the
tables, or else they would get faint for want of
food in looking for them. Under the huge beams
of the roof the tables and benches stood in rank
after rank, as far as the eye could see, like an army
on parade. The cooks always had to use field
glasses when they wanted to see how the men

were getting along with any special dish being
served.

No loggers, before or since, ever ate such wonderful food as did the workers in Paul's camps.
Never was there such a chief cook as Hot Biscuit
Slim, who lorded it over his many assistants like
a king. He quite often forgot to provide some
important item for the menu, it is true, but that
failing could be forgiven him in view of his many
good points. And Sourdough Sam, the chief baker
and flapjack expert, was just as much of an artist
in his field as was Hot Biscuit Slim in that of
general cookery, so that all the men in camp were
never tired of singing their praises.

Such wonderful food was served in Paul's camp
that even the mice benefited from it. Just from
picking up the crumbs that fell from the tables
to the floor, they soon grew so big that they ran
all the wolves out of the country, and the settlers
that came into the Dakotas later on shot them for
tigers.

This mess hall being so big, there was some
trouble at first in getting the food to the tables
while it was still hot, so Paul—who was always
eager to try out new ideas—began to think out some
way of giving quicker service. At first he tried using ponies on roller skates to carry the food to his
men, and wonderful speed they made, but as they

quite often spilled their loads when turning corners he had to give them up and try some other
plan.

He finally built tracks between the rows of
tables and put in freight trains with specially built
cars for carrying the food and got rid of the
ponies. The new plan was successful, except that
there was some trouble in getting the soup to the
tables without sloshing it out. This difficulty was
done away with finally by serving the soup direct
from the boilers where it was made, using six-inch
fire hose for the purpose and fixing a big soup
spigot to serve every five men.

It seems that more food must have been prepared in the Red River Camp than the men could
ever eat, and this would have been true had not
Paul's workers possessed wonderful appetites fully
in keeping with the activities of the cooks. So great
was their ability in this direction that they gave great
astonishment to anyone who was familiar only
with ordinary, normal appetites.

A stranger who once visited the camp was very
much interested in everything he saw and asked
a lot of questions about the things he didn't understand. He was especially puzzled when he saw
a string of big eight-team logging sleds, all heavily
loaded, driving into the cook shanty. He thought
at first that they were hauling in firewood, until he

followed them inside and saw the men unloading the logs and dumping them into a big contrivance through a trap-door from which poured clouds of steam. "That's a mighty funny place to be unloading logs," he remarked to a cook nearby.

"Logs!" exclaimed the cook, with an amused grin on his face. "Gosh, stranger, them ain't logs. Them's sausages for the men's breakfast."

There's no doubt about it, Paul's crews ate a tremendous amount of food, and for a long time all the supplies were carried to the camp by Babe. Once, on one of these trips with food for the camp, Paul got a little careless with Babe. The Great Blue Ox was carrying a load of split peas (this being shortly after Paul had invented the split pea so that his cooks could make twice as much soup out of a load of peas) and his master, thinking of something else and not paying close attention to what he was doing, led the heavily laden animal across a lake where the ice was only six feet thick. Babe, of course, broke through the thin ice and spilled the entire load of peas into the lake.

It looked at first as if the camp would be short of pea soup for a while, which would have been a dreadful calamity, as all of the men were especially fond of their pea soup. Some of them even liked it so well that they hollowed out their peavy handles, and whenever they went out in the woods they would always carry a handleful of pea soup to refresh themselves with between meals.

Paul was accordingly greatly worried for a little while over the prospect of his men having to go for several weeks without their pea soup, but he didn't stay worried long. He just called out the Seven Axmen and the Big Swede, and some of his other good men and put them all under the leadership of Hot Biscuit Slim, the boss cook. They worked around until they pried up the lake enough so that they could build a big fire under it, and they made the peas into soup then and there, later pumping it to the cook shanty through a big fire hose. Thus Paul came through the accident without any loss, and the men liked that soup the best of all because of the fish from the lake that were cooked in it.

The whole thing gave Paul a new idea which saved a lot of trouble from that time on. He had heard of a place where there were a lot of boiling hot springs (maybe it was Yellowstone Park, though one cannot be sure) and he used them for making his pea soup thereafter. He would start off the season by dumping in three or four loads of split peas, throw in the meat from a few big herds of steers which were driven up from Texas for the purpose, and then he would have pea soup, ready cooked, enough to last the whole season. He piped this soup to wherever his camps were, and he never had to worry about that part of feeding his men anymore. It is said that when he finally quit logging in that part of the country, he sold his soup pipe-lines to the Standard Oil Company, who now use them for moving their crude oil across the country.

At first all hands were called to meals by a huge dinner horn which Paul had Ole make for him. It was so big, though, that the first time Paul blew it a whole section of timber fell down, bunkhouses were flattened and many of the men were stunned for a week. So Paul didn't use it very much after that but sounded the call by blowing into a woodpecker's hole in a hollow tree. It is said that he finally sold the big dinner horn to a railroad, which used it in making the roof of a roundhouse.

It was in the Red River Camp that one of Paul's men induced the chief cook to prepare for him a Billdad, which he had killed. Now the Billdad was another one of those strange animals that used to be found in the woods, and there were a number of them in the Dakotas when Paul first went there. The Billdad was not very large, being not much bigger than a beaver, and it was perfectly harmless. It had long, kangaroo-like hind legs, very short front ones, webbed feet, and a heavy, club-like, flat tail which, with its sharp hawk's beak, comprised its only weapons. It lived on fish, and caught its food in a very strange manner. It would sit hunkered down on the bank of a stream or lake until it saw a fish come to the surface, and then it would leap out into the water just ahead of where the ripple had shown and bring down its tail with a loud *thwack!* just as it landed. This would stun the fish, and the Billdad could easily catch it and carry it back to the bank, where it ate it.[1]

As explained before, one of those queer creatures was killed one day by a logger in Paul's camp, and he had the idea that it would make a great delicacy for his supper that evening. So, against the advice of various of his companions, he had Hot Biscuit Slim make a savory stew of it. The poor man had no more than swallowed the first mouthful of it, however, when he let out a strange and fearful cry, his eyes glazed with pain, and he rushed madly from the cook shanty towards the river. When he reached the bank he gave another strange cry, and leaped fifty yards out into the water, hitting the surface in a sitting position much like the Billdad when stunning a fish. Before he could be rescued, he had drowned,

[1] The hind legs of the Billdad were tremendously strong, an adult male having been able to leap sixty yards on an average jump. Needless to say, no lumberjack of to-day will so much as touch one of these animals, even with a pike pole.

[103]

and since that time no one has ever tried eating one of these animals. After this sad occurrence, Paul Bunyan gave strict orders that none of the cooks was ever to prepare special dishes for any of the hands but that everyone would have to be content with the food that was served to all alike.

One may think, from the care which Paul took to see that his men were comfortable and well fed, that eating was the main occupation in his Red River Camp. Nothing could be farther from the truth. His camp was no logger's dream of Paradise, nor was there ever any loafing or luxury in it.

Paul worked his men twelve hours a day, and they would have been surprised and ashamed to have put in any less time. Nature had given them great sturdy bodies and hearts that were full of daring, and they loved the tremendous exertions of their tasks and the dangers of their hazardous work, so that they would have been bored with an easier life. Each one took great pride in doing his share toward Paul's accomplishments, and to say that they fully merited the high wages paid them and the food and lodging supplied to them is stating no more than the exact truth.

The mere fact that Paul Bunyan and his men cleared off all the trees from two big states, delivered the logs to the mills, and even got rid of

Soon after Elmer, the Moose Terrier, had learned to move freely with his hind legs on backwards, he brought home a young half-grown and remarkably ugly Whirling Whimpus

the stumps that were left, doing all this mighty task in just one winter, is ample proof of how hard everyone labored. Being hearty workers made them hearty eaters, and all the trouble Paul took in seeing that they were satisfied was no more than they deserved and was clearly his plain duty. There were no useless frills about any of his camps—that is certain—and from the tremendous work that was done in the Dakotas it can be seen that everything in the Red River Camp was carefully planned with an accurate eye toward achieving the greatest efficiency.

IX

Paul Bunyan Logs
Off the Dakotas

IT was at his famous Red River Camp in North
Dakota that Paul Bunyan began to work
along the more systematic lines which changing
conditions were causing him to adopt. Other op-
erators were following in his footsteps, though
of course they did their logging on a much smaller
scale, and were establishing camps here and there
over the country. In order that his logs might never
get mixed up with those of anyone else, Paul began marking everyone cut by his men. Nowadays
lumbermen mark their logs with big lumber cray-
ons made especially for that purpose, but Paul put
his mark on each of his logs by pinching a big
piece out of it with his fingers.

It was about this time, too, that he invented the
bookkeeping system for lumber camps that has

been used ever since. His operations in the Dakotas, and afterwards, were on such a big scale that it became too much trouble for him to keep all the details in his head, though he probably could have remembered everything that went into the books if he had found it necessary to do so. So it was that Johnny Inkslinger made his appearance among the great logger's helpers and served with the utmost faithfulness through many years.

Johnny Inkslinger was the first lumber camp bookkeeper, or camp clerk, and he was a most efficient person. During his first winter with Paul, his marvelous ability saved his employer a good many dollars in various ways. For instance, he hit on the plan of leaving the dots from the *i*'s and the crosses from the *t*'s when writing in the camp books, and in this manner saved Paul nine barrels of ink on the payroll alone. There was never a shortage of pay in camp while he was in charge of the books, and never an overcharge, although he alone had to keep the records of thousands of men and complete reports of the millions of feet of logs that were cut. He used six barrels of ink a week just in the addition of figures alone, and no one knows how many more in his multiplication and subtraction and the thousands of letters he had to write. He always wrote with a fountain pen which he had invented himself and which was attached to a barrel of ink by a hose. Once the ink started running through his pen, he never stopped writing until the barrel ran dry.

In addition to his bookkeeping, he was also the camp dentist and doctor, and as such he made many wonderful cures that would puzzle the most expert specialist of today. Altogether, he had so much to do that it was lucky he needed only four hours of sleep a week, which gave him more time for work than the average man cares to think about.

It was during this period that Paul Bunyan made his greatest reputation, for it was in the Dakotas and the Lake States afterwards that he did most of those things which have made his name one that will always endure. It is positively known that he logged off North and South Dakota—for who else could have removed the trees so cleanly from those states?—and that he did it all in one winter. Also, he did all the work from one camp, for no remains of logging camps have ever been found farther west than the Red River. This was a record for even such a mighty man as he, and he was able to accomplish such a task chiefly because of the help he received from the Seven Axmen. Babe, the Great Blue Ox, did heroic service, of course, and so did the Big Swede, Johnny Inkslinger and in fact every member of the mighty crew. His chief helpers in all, however, were the Seven Ax-men, and by their labors that winter they proved themselves to be just about the greatest woods-men that ever lived. Knowing the heroic deeds they performed, no one can doubt that the Dakotas were logged off in just one winter, for the efficiency of these gigantic cousins was such that more time in which to do the task could not possibly have been used.

Paul had used the ax-handle in the east and continued to supply handles for all of his men except the Seven Axmen. These great fellows he equipped with enormous double-bitted ax-heads, tied to long cables instead of being on handles. The method used by the Axmen was to stride forward in line with one another, swinging their axes in great circles as they advanced. At each swing they cut down a section of timber as a scythe cuts down a swathe of grain. Since the trees all leaned so that they fell evenly and didn't get tangled to-gether, the gangs that followed the Axmen made fast progress in cutting the fallen trunks into the proper lengths for logs and piling them for skid-ding to the river.

Paul occasionally got out his three-mile crosscut saw, and with the Little Chore Boy holding down the other end, he also felled vast stretches of the leaning pines. He had so many other things to look after, however, that he worked with his saw only part of the time, trusting to the Seven Axmen to do most of the felling, and well did they live up to his faith in them. It is said that his crews cut over a million feet of logs a day during that winter in the Dakotas, and most of this work was done by the Seven Axmen. Each of the Axmen had five fleet-footed helpers who did nothing but carry dulled axes back to camp and bring out fresh, keen ones again.

The problem of keeping the Seven Axmen's blades sharp was at first a troublesome one. There were no hills in the Dakotas steep enough for them to sharpen axes as they had done in Maine, and so a new way had to be found. "Well," said Paul to himself, "since we can't use stones as they roll down hill, why can't we have a big stone that can be turned while it stays in one place?" So he smoothed off a great flat piece of rock, shaped it perfectly round, and made a square hole for a handle in the center so that it could be swung up onto a trestle and turned by hand. Thus was the problem solved by Paul's invention of the grindstone, a most valuable invention as everyone will agree.

He had bad luck with the first two grindstones he made, though. The first one he laid aside after shaping the stone as he wanted it, intending to put the handle on it after he finished making a trestle to hold it. While he was working on the trestle, Hard-jaw Murphy, one of his men, came around the corner of the tool house smacking his lips and picking his teeth with a peavy. "That's a mighty good brand of cheese you're getting for this camp now, Mr. Bunyan," he grinned. "I jest found a hull cheese back yonder a piece, and et it all up," and he winked his eye in high good humor, proud of having gotten ahead of the camp steward who was very watchful of victuals between meals.

"Cheese!" exclaimed Paul, rather put out. "That wasn't a cheese, you dunderhead. That was my new grindstone!" and as punishment he set the astounded logger to shaping another stone just like the one he had made away with.

The second grindstone was soon finished and mounted, and it was a very large affair. It did the work of sharpening tools quickly and well, and was very popular with all in camp except the Little Chore Boy, whose task it was to turn it. He finally got so tired of sharpening axes with it that one day he became very angry and threw it out of sight.

Paul came along a few minutes later and saw that his new invention was missing. "What has happened to the grindstone?" he asked in surprise.

"I got tired of turning the thing, so I threw it

away," said the Little Chore Boy, sullenly. Indeed, he had flung it so hard and thrown it so far that it had sailed clear across Minnesota and landed in northern Wisconsin, where it sank deep into the earth, digging an enormous hole. The great scar it made when it fell later filled with water and became Grindstone Lake, as anyone can easily see from a map.

"Oh, well, it doesn't matter very much that it's gone," said Paul, his eyes twinkling. "It was getting too small to do the work, anyway." So the Little Chore Boy didn't gain anything, after all, for the very next day Paul made a new grindstone that was much bigger and harder to turn than the other one had been. It is said that this new one was so big that every time it turned around three times it was pay day again.

In all of Paul's work in the Dakotas Babe, as always, proved of great help to his master. There were some districts which were far from any stream that was big enough to float logs, and so Paul thought of a way to use the Great Blue Ox's tremendous strength in getting this timber nearer water. He would hitch Babe to a full section of land and drag the whole thing, trees and all, down to the river right handy to the camp. There Paul's men would cut the timber from it, pile the logs on the banks of the stream, and then Babe would haul the cleared square mile of land back to its proper place again. In this way Paul was able to log sections that he otherwise never would have bothered about and never would have been able to touch without the unique assistance of the Great Blue Ox.

It took Babe just one day to haul six sections of land down to the river and then take them back again after the trees had been cut off. That made thirty-six sections a week. The first week, however, that this plan was put into use Paul had the Ox haul Section Thirty-seven down the last thing on Saturday night, intending to leave it there over Sunday and clear it off the first thing on Monday morning. On Sunday the river rose, washed the section away, and it has never been found since. That is why all government survey maps today show only thirty-six sections to a township, as Paul Bunyan lost Section Thirty-seven and never recovered it again.

And so, his mighty crew working in all directions with a vigor and efficiency that has never been equaled, Paul Bunyan progressed rapidly through the winter with his task of logging off the Dakotas. Finally, as spring came on, he suddenly discovered that all the big timber of the two states had been cut off and that some of his men had even worked down into Nebraska and Kansas, clearing off all the trees as they went. Hastily ordering everyone to cease work, he reassembled his men once more at the big camp to await his next orders.

Throughout the Dakotas all the timber that was now to be found was a few patches, here and there, of small trees not big enough for logs. He looked around for a market for these, and found it with a railroad that was just being built across the country. The railroad needed wooden ties for its tracks, so Paul turned most of his men into tie-hacks, or tie-cutters, and proceeded to dispose of all his small timber in the form of railroad ties. He trained the cutters to climb the trees with forty-pound broadaxes strapped to their feet like skates, scoring great slashes in the sides of the trees as they went up. Once at the top, they would slide down again, the heavy blades on their feet slicing off the wood on opposite sides of the trees, hewing two flat faces at once so that the timber was just of the right thickness. After they had learned, also, to cut off a tie every eight feet as they slid down, they worked very fast, having only to climb up a tree and slide back down in order to manufacture it into railroad ties.

Finally, even all the small trees were used in this manner, the ties hauled away, the logs delivered long ago to the sawmills, and the camp cleaned up. Nothing was left of the great forests that had stood on these vast stretches of fertile land excepting the stumps, and Paul soon got rid of them. He picked out the very strongest men in his crew and armed them all with heavy wooden mallets. Then, he himself leading the way, they started out. One blow was enough to drive the biggest stump far down into the ground, and so *thump! thump!* faster than anyone could count, Paul's men pounded all the stumps out of sight into the earth. It was only a day or two until there was not a stump left in sight, nor a tree either—nothing but miles and miles of rolling plains where once the forests had stood and the Hugags roamed. The work in the Dakotas was finished and Paul Bunyan was ready to move on to other fields.

The Senator who had hired him was very much pleased with the work and thanked him in a speech so long that it could be repeated only in the *Congressional Record*. Before summer had come, the two states were being settled by the Swedish farmers who had been driven out of their own country, and they soon made fine farms where the leaning pines had stood so thickly only a year before. That's why, today, there are so many Swedes in North and South Dakota, thanks to the great work of Paul Bunyan.

X

Paul Bunyan's Pets

FROM Paul's wonderful success in training Babe, the Great Blue Ox, it can easily be seen how truly remarkable was the great logger's understanding and liking toward animals. He was exceedingly fond of pets and throughout his life he had many of them, some of them very strange creatures indeed. Of course, none of them ever crowded Babe from first place in the affections of their master, although there are several other of Paul's pets which have become almost as well known as the Great Blue Ox.

There were Jerry and Jinny, the Mule Team, for instance, which had proven so useful in the matter of transporting the big flapjack griddle from place to place. And then also there had been Willie, the Little Blue Ox. Paul had sorrowed greatly when the Little Blue Ox had met his dreadful fate, and it was only a little later that he purchased Bessie, The Yaller Cow, in hopes that the new animal would fill the place left vacant by Willie's sad demise.

Bessie was a very wonderful animal, much more useful than Willie had ever been, and she made up for his loss so well that in a very short time Paul had grown remarkably fond of her. She was possessed of numerous good qualities, none of which was more valuable than her remarkable faculty for giving milk. She gave so much milk that it kept seven men busy just skimming the cream from it.

It is a sad fact, though, that Paul did not have her very long before he almost caused her to lose her value as a dairy animal. He didn't have fodder enough in camp to feed her as she should have been fed, and so he taught her to graze on pine branches and needles, with an occasional feast of baled hay, as Babe had been doing for many years. As a result of her new diet her milk soon became too strong to be used for food, and so Paul had to discover another use for it. The solution of the problem was very simple; he had all the cream churned into butter, and when the snow and ice melted off the roads in the early spring he kept his logging roads slippery and in good condition by greasing them thickly with Bessie's butter. Thus, after he secured the Yaller Cow, he was able to extend the logging season as far into the summer of each year as he wished.

Bessie's unvaried feeding upon pine needles seemed, after a while, to have an ill effect upon her, and she began to get thin and scrawny. Her master was greatly worried over her condition, and had Johnny Inkslinger try out all his favorite remedies in hopes of arousing a new interest in life within her. All that was done, however, proved futile, until by chance a queer affliction to which she was subject brought about the experiment which cured her.

The Yaller Cow's eyes were very weak, and the bright glare of the snow made her snow-blind after she had been turned out of doors for several days, so Paul rigged her up with a pair of grass-green goggles as a protection. One may imagine his surprise when from that time on she began to grow fat and healthy once more. The goggles, besides keeping the brightness of the snow from hurting her eyes, made everything look like grass to her. After Paul fitted her out also with a pair of snowshoes, she would be turned out every day among the gleaming drifts. There she would wander about contentedly, feeding heartily upon the drifted snow under the impression that it was the sweetest and tenderest of meadow grass.

One other pet which Paul Bunyan had, and one

which is almost as well known as Babe, was Elmer, the Moose Terrier, a dog so big and strong that he could kill a moose with one shake as easily as a fox terrier kills a rat. Elmer met with a serious accident one night which came near putting an end to his career. He had slipped into the dark bunkhouse and was making a bed for himself among some old clothes in the corner when Paul heard the slight noise.

"There's another one of those pesky rats!" he growled to himself, and hurled his ax as hard as he could in the direction of the sound. He was a very sorrowful man, indeed, when a moment or two later he made a light and saw what he had done. He had hurled his ax at Elmer instead of a rat, and the flying blade had hit the dog squarely in the middle, slicing him in half just as nicely as you please.

Paul got busy at once trying to save the poor animal's life. He succeeded in getting the two parts joined together again and sewed up nicely, and so fast did he work and such a good job did he do that Elmer recovered. In his great hurry, though, Paul had put the hind quarters on the wrong way, so that the dog's hind legs stuck straight up in the air, in just the opposite direction from the front ones. Thus the poor animal had two feet pointing down and two pointing up, no matter on which pair he stood.

When the great Moose Terrier finally recovered, he found it rather difficult to move about with any degree of speed, owing to his new fore-and-aft construction. Paul missed the dog greatly every time he went hunting, and finally he called Shot Gunderson to him and gave him some instructions. "I want you to go out in the woods and catch a Tote-Road Shagamaw for me," he ordered. "Bring it back to camp alive, without hurting or scaring it in any way, and perhaps we can persuade Elmer to adopt the Shagamaw's method of traveling."

There was something to Paul's plan, and Shot Gunderson nodded his head in agreement as he set off on his errand. The Tote-Road Shagamaw was a very queer animal, he knew. In fact, it was one of the queerest creatures in the woods, and he agreed that its unique peculiarities should make it a most desirable companion for Elmer in his present crippled condition.

The Shagamaw, like the injured dog, had his hind- and fore-legs pointing in different directions also. He had made the most of his disability, however, and had even developed it into a valuable quality. Both pairs of legs could never be used at the same time, and so when the Tote-Road Shagamaw walked along it would travel first on the front pair, with the hind ones sticking up into the air. Then, when the front legs became tired, it would reverse and travel for a while on its hind pair while it gave the others a rest.

This caused a lot of puzzlement and bewilderment among woodsmen, for the reason that the Shagamaw's front feet were those of a bear and its hind feet were exactly like the hooves of a moose. Thus, when it walked and shifted from one set of legs to the other, moose tracks and bear tracks would very strangely take the place of one another. This was, of course, puzzling and disgusting to the average person. A moose hunter would lose all interest when he suddenly found that the moose he had been trailing had evidently been suddenly devoured by a bear, and a bear hunter would give up the chase in bewilderment when he strangely discovered that what he thought were bear tracks were really moose tracks in the last analysis.[1]

Shot Gunderson, however, was too experienced a hunter to be fooled by such shifting about, and

[1] *Bipedester delusissimus* is the name by which the Tote-Road Shagamaw is known to science. This creature was at one time quite plentiful in the woods, but of recent years it has become very scarce. The last one to be seen by a reputable authority was discovered in Maine in the spring of 1901. When seen, the animal was solemnly following a range line through the woods, marking off first an exact quarter mile of bear tracks, and then a quarter mile of moose tracks with great precision.

it was not long before he discovered moose hoof-prints which suddenly changed into the tracks of a bear, and he knew at once that he had discovered the path of a Tote-Road Shagamaw.

When the strange animal had been captured and brought into camp, Paul soon managed to establish it on friendly terms with Elmer. The Moose Terrier was a very smart dog, indeed, and he eyed his new companion with the greatest interest. It was not strange, therefore, that a very short time later Elmer began to imitate the strange manner in which the Shagamaw was accustomed to walking, and before many days had passed he had become very proficient in his new method of getting over the ground.

Thus the Moose Terrier came through his dreadful accident better off than he had been before. After he had mastered his new method of traveling he never grew tired. He could run on his front legs until they became weary and then turn over and use the other pair while he rested the tired ones, in this manner keeping himself always fresh even through hours of strenuous running. He soon became a better hunting dog than ever before, for he could outrun anything in the woods and he never grew tired.

It was shortly after Elmer had recovered from his mishap that he one day came dragging into

camp one of the strangest creatures that Paul had
ever seen. This was a young, half-grown and remarkably ugly Whirling Whimpus, the only one of
its kind that is known ever to have been captured
alive. At first it was of a very amiable disposition
and became quite affectionate towards Paul, but
as it grew a little older it gradually began to
manifest that inborn hatred toward mankind
which is perhaps the strongest characteristic of
this species of animal.

The Whimpus is a creature of no mean pro-
portions. It stands head and shoulders above the
size of a tall man, has a gorilla-shaped head, a villainous black face and a barrel body from which
project long slender arms supporting enormous
heavy hands. Its unique method of obtaining its
food when hungry accounts for the fear in which
it is held by all who are familiar with its habits.
It will station itself upon a trail or tote-road,
usually just around a bend in some well-traveled
path, and there it will stand upon its diminutive
and pivot-like hind legs, stretch out its long arms,
and begin to whirl like a top. It gradually in-
creases its whirling speed until at last the animal
is whirling so fast that it has become invisible,
making no more than a slight blur in the air. The
motion produces a strange droning sound that
seems to come from the trees overhead, and any

creature approaching along the trail is totally un-
aware of the waiting danger.

There the Whimpus stands and whirls, making
his queer buzzing hunger call, until finally some
unlucky person walks into his unseen presence.
The beast's great hands, outstretched and being
thrown about with such mighty whirling force, hit
the newcomer with a mighty smack and demolish
him utterly with instantaneous ease. The poor man
is deposited upon the huge paws of the Whimpus
in the form of a varnish or jelly, and the hungry
animal can lick it off at his leisure.

Paul's young Whimpus did not at first show any
dangerous traits, and for a time he was a great favorite among all the men in camp. Then, as he grew
a little larger, he began to manifest an inclination
toward whirling. It was but natural that he should,
sooner or later, give way to his inborn tendencies in
that direction, and though his master attempted to
break him of the desire, the creature persisted in
trying to make a top of himself. Soon he was whirling about camp with a rapidity which endangered
the lives of the men, and Paul grew apprehensive
as to the advisability of trying further to make a
pet out of such a dangerous creature.

Finally the Whirling Whimpus gave way completely to the ferocious instincts of his kind and
spun himself into invisibility right on the main

street of the camp. There, sad to state, he jellied and devoured four of the workers who happened to come by within reach of his flailing paws.

"There's nothing to do but to get rid of that animal at once," said Paul regretfully, "but it certainly is a pity to see all of that tremendous power being lost in whirling."

"Well, Mr. Bunyan," broke in Johnny Inkslinger, the efficient and capable camp clerk, "if I may offer a suggestion, we—ahem—may be able to get rid of the Whirling Whimpus and at the same time utilize him creating for the camp something which it long has needed." He went on further to explain, in the greatest detail, the plan he had in mind, and so well did Paul like the idea that he started putting it to work at once.

First of all, be it known, the Dakota camp was badly in need of a dependable water supply. The cooks could hardly get enough water for all their kitchen needs, Babe and the other animals of the camp found it difficult to get enough to drink, and in general the camp was suffering from the lack of a big central supply of water. It was with this pressing need that Johnny Inkslinger's suggestion had to do.

Paul ordered Ole, the smith, to make for him an augur, a tremendous big boring bit of a queer stubby design. When at last the new augur was completed, Paul carried it out to the summit of a high sandhill near camp, leading the Whirling Whimpus shambling along behind him.

Most of the men of the camp had learned that something interesting was about to take place, and they crowded about at a safe distance to see what was going on. They watched Paul place the new augur in a slight depression in the ground, so that the point was firmly started downwards. They grinned expectantly when he next induced the Whimpus to place his hind feet upon special footrests that had been prepared and quickly and firmly lashed the beast to the augur bit. Then, with some apprehension as to the dependability of the bonds that held the animal, they quickly withdrew beyond range of the Whimpus' long arms and watched the creature's frantic struggles to release itself.

Unable to free himself, the beast began to howl with rage, and he kept growing angrier and angrier until there seemed no bounds for his outburst. Then all at once he thrust his long arms out sideways and began to whirl. Faster and faster he went, and faster and faster did his whirling make the sharp augur bit at his feet drive down into the earth, so that within a moment or two the terrible creature had disappeared entirely. All that was left was a great, gaping round hole straight down into the ground from the top of the hill and from which there poured a stream of fresh dirt and sand like ashes from a volcano.

"Yumpin' yiminy!" yelled the Big Swede, in an excess of emotion. "He bane gone clean through to Chiny, sure!"

And, indeed, the Swede may have been right. For a while the new well which the Whirling Whimpus had bored was filled with water and furnished the camp with all that was needed. This well was so deep that it took all day for the buckets to fall to the water and a week to haul them up again, and it was so broad that hundreds of buckets could be run at once without getting into the way of one another.

It was not very long, however, until the water in the new well began to fail, and finally it disappeared altogether. Every one figured that the Whimpus had just kept right on boring his way through the earth until he finally pushed himself out, feet first, into China on the other side of the world and that the water from the well flowed out in the same direction.

Of course, after it went dry, the well was abandoned, and no further care was taken of it. As the years went by, the soil and sand blew away from around it, so that today there is about a hundred and fifty feet of it sticking up into the air, making a striking landmark.

"Hooray!" the fisherman yelled, *"I've caught a Squonk!"*

It was after his well proved a failure that Paul Bunyan made Lake Superior as a watering place for the Great Blue Ox, and from that time on the big animal always had all he wanted to drink. Actual proof of Babe's size can be had just by looking at Lake Superior, for though the Great Blue Ox is no longer in existence, the lake still is. Paul was rather proud of this piece of work, and it is said that always afterward he wore as a watch charm the shovel with which he had dug the lake.

Water from the camp was also carried from Lake Superior, after Paul had completed it, for no place else could the Little Chore Boy find water deep enough for him to dip the camp bucket in it. As his bucket was always leaking, the water he lost ran together in the hollows of the ground and made most of the ten thousand lakes that today lie in northern Minnesota between Lake Superior and the Red River. The Mississippi River is also said to have risen from this same source, proof of which can be had just by visiting St. Paul or Minneapolis, past which the river may be seen running, even today.

The Little Chore Boy carried all the water used in camp, and he went back and forth several times each day. He became greatly disgusted with his leaky bucket, but he never got a new one to replace it until after his amusing experience with the

Big Wind. He was going back to camp with a bucketful of water when the Big Wind came up, and it blew so hard that it was all he could do to keep from being blown away. He kept on his feet, however, and kept tight hold on his bucket of water, so that finally he made his way safely back to camp. It was not until he started to pour the water he had brought into the tea-kettle, though, that he found out what a remarkable feat he had performed. He had carried the water into camp without spilling a drop of it, in spite of the fact that the Big Wind had blown so hard that it had blown away every one of the weakened staves of the old bucket from around its contents.

XI

Paul's Bad Luck

Fʀᴏᴍ the Dakotas, after he had completed his contracts there, Paul Bunyan moved over into the Lake States. It is said that he stepped across the Minnesota line carrying his big grindstone under one arm, and Elmer, his famous fore-and-aft Moose Terrier, under the other in order to balance the weight. Babe, the Great Blue Ox, and Bessie, the Yaller Cow, were driven on ahead. Babe was laden with all the camp equipment, tools and other property that had to be moved, while Bessie carried only a church bell around her neck so that she could be located by its sound when she got lost, as her poor eyesight quite often caused her to go astray in spite of the green goggles which she always wore.

Behind Paul there trailed a long line of loggers bearing their turkeys or blanket rolls, for most of his Dakota crew moved eastward with him. A wonderful parade they all made through the wilderness, and it was a shame that no one had a chance to see it pass except the wild creatures of the woods.

Paul did not take his big flapjack griddle with him on his first trip, but came back and got it later. First of all, he located a place for his permanent camp, and got all his men started on the building of the shanties, bunkhouses, stables and other shelters which would be needed. Not until then did he hitch up Jerry and Jinny, his famous Mule Team, and go after the griddle. Some authorities say that he moved the griddle to the new location by hitching his team to the land the Red River Camp was on, hauling the entire camp, buildings, griddle and all, to the new location. It is more likely, however, that he moved just the griddle, as most of his Red River Camp buildings would have been far too small to serve in his new camp.

In his Red River Camp he had found the big flapjack so hard to handle that from now on he had Sourdough Sam fix up the hot cake rations for the camp in a little different way. Instead of making one big flapjack, the cooks now began making a lot of little ones not more than three or four feet across. Forty to fifty of these would be tied together in a bundle, and the ration was one bundle to a man—though there were always a few hearty eaters that came back for a second helping. Paul extended the railroad tracks from the mess hall to the griddle, and when the flapjacks began getting brown, the trains would run on regular express service. Each car would be loaded down with bales of flapjacks, and a couple of waiters in asbestos suits would perch themselves on top. Then, as they whizzed down the line of tables, they would toss a bale to each man as they went past. This new system saved so much time at breakfast that the men were able to be in the woods long before daylight.

Paul established his camp on the Big Onion River near where the Little Augur flows into it. From this central location he worked all the Lake States, logging off most of the white pine forests of Minnesota, Wisconsin and Michigan. His work in the Dakotas had made him enthusiastic about logging on a grand scale, and his operations now began to be probably the greatest ever seen, even surpassing those done from his Red River Camp.

During the first year, however, that Paul was in his Big Onion Camp, he was not able to get very much timber cut. Bad luck seemed to follow him that year, and a number of extraordinary misfortunes fell upon him to delay his work. Because of the evil that dogged his footsteps, his crews were hardly ever able to cut more than a million feet of logs a day and some days not even that.

In the first place, Paul had selected a location that was rather a poor one for logging, although the timber that stretched for hundreds of miles around was the thickest and largest he had yet seen. The Big Onion River was a treacherous stream and a very hard one to send a drive of logs over. Also, the hills over which the logs had to be skidded were so rugged that they tested even the Great Blue Ox's enormous strength.

Worst of all, though, was the rank growth of wild onions that covered nearly every foot of ground between the trees, and gave the name of "Big Onion" to the nearby river. Their juicy green tops grew higher than onions have ever been known to grow before, reaching above a tall man's chin. They got in the way every time a logger tried to swing an ax, and stopped nearly all attempts at felling trees. Their juice, crushed from them by trampling feet and swinging axes, spread its strength and savor upon the air, bringing such floods of blinding tears to the eyes of everyone within its range that hardly anything could be done. Onion flavor seasoned everyone so strongly that the men could hardly stand to live with one another, and worst of all a man could hardly stand to live with himself.

Under such conditions, it was dangerous for a man even to try to use a sharp tool like an ax, and Shot Gunderson came near being badly injured in this way. He had started out hunting, as the meat already in camp had become so strongly flavored with onion that the men could no longer eat it, and he had stopped on a hillside to try and rub the onion juice from his streaming eyes. He failed to see a blinded logger come stumbling up the slope toward him, nor did he hear the newcomer's remark of, "This here looks like a good stick," as he swung his ax with all his might.

It was not until the surprised hunter's yell burst on his ears that the befuddled axman realized his error. Being able to see but faintly, he had mistaken Shot's leg for the trunk of a pine tree, and only the fact that the hunter was wearing high, heavy leather boots saved him from a painful injury.

Paul Bunyan soon became very much discouraged by such a state of things. "I've a good notion to move to another part of the country," he said to his bookkeeper, as he wiped the onion-tears from his eyes. "These vegetables have just about made me ready to run away, though I never thought until now that anything could make me feel that way."

"Wait just a little longer," pleaded Johnny Inkslinger. "When we first came here, I conceived an idea as to how a profitable use might be made of these same onions that are causing so much trouble. I'm sure, Mr. Bunyan, that if you will wait just a short time longer, you will soon begin to see the results of my cogitation."

"All right, Johnny," Paul answered him. "I have a great deal of faith in you, and so I'll wait a little while longer before moving camp, but I can't stand very much more of this fragrance. Why, already my men have shed so many tears that the Big Onion has risen out of its banks. Here we have a regular freshet running down the river and no logs for it to carry to the mills. I'm getting plumb disgusted."

But Johnny was right. When his plan began to show results, as it did just a few days later, Paul was very glad he had listened to his efficient book-keeper. Johnny Inkslinger had heard of the failure of the garlic crop in Italy that year, and unbeknownst to anyone else he had gotten in touch with the high officials of the Italian government and made a contract with them. They sent over many shiploads of experienced garlic diggers, and these worked industriously in the woods all along the Big Onion River, uprooting the wild onions and drying them for shipment back to their own country, where they took the place of the garlic so badly needed there and arrived just in time to prevent a very serious revolution. Almost before one could realize it there was not a single wild onion left in the woods. Paul was so pleased that he raised Johnny Inkslinger's wages and then set about getting his work into shape again.

The great logger had hardly gotten things to running smoothly again when the work was once more held up, this time by the coming of the Big Fog. The fog drifted down over the country one night, and for several weeks it was like a thick cottony blanket covering the land. It was so thick that the fish in the river were unable to tell where the river left off and the fog began, and many thousands of them—swimming around in the fog and thinking they were still in the river—became lost in the woods and were left stranded among the trees far from water when the fog finally went down. Paul's men all had to wear mosquito netting over their heads in order to keep the pollywogs out of their faces.

The fog was so thick that while it lasted any cutting of timber was almost out of the question, and so all of the men in camp began devising various sports to help pass the time away. Their favorite game was a fishing contest, which helped to while away many dull hours during the Big Fog.

In this contest several men would carry big gunny sacks to a favorite spot, and stand there, holding the mouths of the sacks wide open. Then they would begin to imitate the cries and calls which the fish made as they swam around through the fog, and the man who enticed the most fish into his bag won the contest.

Once one of the men heard a queer wailing sound some distance away, and thinking that it was some new kind of fish, he began mocking its cries. It came nearer and nearer, and finally he enticed it into his bag. He could tell immediately from the feel of it through the bag that the creature was not a fish, and from the roughness of its loose and bumpy skin he was able very shortly to learn what he had captured. "Hooray!" he yelled to his companions, "I've caught a Squonk!" and despite the poor animal's desperate wailings he bundled it under his arm and hurried with it to the bunkhouse. He was greatly excited over his unusual catch, which was indeed a prize, and he looked forward to enjoying the importance which the display of it to his fellows would give him.

The Squonk, which is one of the rarest animals in the woods, is a very shy creature, and its retiring disposition is due to the shame which it feels on account of its unlovely appearance. It has dull red eyes, a long comical nose, and an ill-fitting warty skin, as well as several other blemishing defects, on account of all of which it intensely dislikes being seen. Because it yearns to be beautiful, and yet is condemned to be so fearfully ugly, it is always unhappy and weeps and wails constantly, leaving a trail of tears wherever it goes. So rarely did it ever get near men that the logger who had caught the Squonk was greatly elated, and called all his friends to the bunkhouse to see the queer creature when he put it on view. When he opened the bag, however, there was nothing there except some salt water and bubbles. The poor creature, made more unhappy than ever by being caught, and being so fearful of being seen in all its homeliness, had simply dissolved in tears.[1]

At one time during the Big Fog the mist began to leak through the cook shanty roof, so Paul called out some of his men and set them to nailing on more shingles. When the fog finally cleared away, there was a great crash where the men had done their work, and they saw then what they had done. The thickness of the fog had confused them, and instead of nailing the shingles on the cook shanty roof, as they thought they were doing, they

[1] *Lacrimacorpus dissolvens* is the descriptive as well as the scientific name of the Squonk. In hunting the animal, the best time is on cold, moonlight nights, when the animal sheds its tears slowly and dislikes moving about. The tears freeze as they fall, thus leaving a trail that is very easy to follow. Hemlock forests are the Squonk's favorite habitat, and often these creatures may be heard wailing where the gloomy hemlocks stand dark and thick.

had nailed them out onto the fog itself which, of course, let the new roof collapse when its support began to disappear.

Paul Bunyan finally figured out a way to get rid of the Big Fog. He hitched Babe up to a great plow, made a lot of ditches, and drained the fog right back into the river.

The Big Fog was probably the cause of the immense mosquitoes that soon afterwards began to appear. They swarmed through the woods in ever-increasing numbers, and became a real menace to the workmen in Paul's camp. One of the few mistakes which the great logger ever made was when he thought out the plan of fighting off the mosquitoes with bumble bees. He sent away for a lot of extra big bees and turned them loose, expecting them to get rid of the pests in no time at all, but instead of fighting them the bees made friends with the mosquitoes. They became so friendly that they intermarried, and the young bee-mosquitoes that resulted were worse than their parents, for they had a sting at both ends.

Those youngsters were terrors, and they made life not only miserable, but dangerous, for every one in the woods. Paul had to put extra guards, with pike poles, peavies and axes for weapons, into the stables to fight the insects away from the ani-

mals when they succeeded in tearing the shakes
off of the roof so that they could get in.

This new crop of gigantic insects was so large
that there was not nearly enough for them to eat,
after they finished killing off all the wild animals
in the woods nearby. As a result of their ferocious
instincts, it was not long before they became so
dangerous that a man was taking his life in his
hands if he even went out of doors.

Paul finally managed to play a trick on them,
though, that got rid of most of them. He sneaked
a lot of men down into the fire hole under the big
flapjack griddle and then barricaded the place
they had come in. The swarm of bee-mosquitoes
settled down thick all over the griddle, smelling
the men underneath and tried their best with
both stingers to bore their way to where the men
were.

Paul waited until the insects had their stingers
wedged deeply into the steel, and then he and
his men had an easy time killing them off with axes
and clubs, as their weapons were rammed tightly
into the griddle and they couldn't fight back. They
nearly ruined the big griddle, though, and it later
had to be turned over so the other side could be
used. The stingers had punctured the first side so
full of big holes that the cook-boys would have

been in great danger of falling in as they skated around to grease the griddle.

After these ferocious creatures had been subdued, Paul and his men heaved great sighs of relief, thinking that their bad luck was over and that they would soon be getting the Big Onion Camp to running along on its expected schedule. Winter was at hand, and everyone set about putting everything into the best of shape in hope of securing a record cut of logs during the months to come.

XII

The Winter of the Blue Snow

As the weather began to turn cold, Paul felt sure that his bad luck had left him, and he began to make great plans as to how he would regain all the time that had been lost. He was quite happy when the thermometer showed a lower mark each succeeding day, and he looked forward with impatience for the snows to begin.

When the first snow did come, however, he began to lose his enthusiasm. There was something so strange about the flakes that he was filled with new foreboding as soon as they began to fall. They were a bright *blue* in color, and once started, they fell unceasingly.

That winter has always been remembered by loggers as the Winter of the Blue Snow, for never before or after—so far as history shows or the oldest man can remember—has there ever been any other snow of that color. So much of it fell that finally Paul had to let his men down on ropes before they could find even the tops of the tallest trees, and, of course, not much logging could be done. The snow stopped falling at last, and then the weather turned cold, and so cold was it that men afterwards spoke of it as the Year of the Two Winters, since it was as cold as two winters put together.

It was so cold that the men were worse troubled by Snow-Snakes and pesky little Frostbiters than ever before. Nearly every step they would take out of doors, there would be a Snow-Snake waiting all coiled up and ready to strike. Once it sank its fangs into a person, he was a goner, sure, for he would freeze to death before help could come. The Frostbiters were not fatal, but they were really an awful nuisance.

It certainly was cold that winter, so cold that men's words froze and dropped to the ground as they were spoken. Johnny Inkslinger had to work out a brand new system for interpreting them before the members of the crew could talk to one another, and a little later a special frozen-word interpreter had to be imported into the camp.

As in every camp, the Big Onion Camp had a few trouble finders who were always kicking about

various things. Paul made all these chronic kickers
meet in a special fault-finding conference every day
and relieve themselves of all their unpleasant crit-
icisms at that time. Of course their words froze
and dropped to the ground as fast as they were
spoken, and as nobody could hear them until after
they were thawed out, the fault-finders never troubled themselves to speak mildly. Paul had all
of their frozen words gathered up into a big bin,
intending to haul such troublesome rubbish far
away from camp and bury it, until the ever-effi-
cient Johnny Inkslinger thought of boxing up the
most explosive of all the words and selling them
for blasting powder. They were very powerful,
too, when a charge of them was set off all at once.

One good thing which the cold spell did was
to cure all the men in camp of swearing. Whenever a man dropped a cuss-word, Paul had it
picked up by a special crew for the purpose, la-
beled with the man's name, and stored away.
When spring came and the weather began to get
warm, each man that had a bale of cuss-words
saved up for him had to take them all out and
listen to them as they thawed. Some wonderful
combinations were heard along about that time,
and having to sit back and listen to their full
winter's cussing all in one bunch was a most sat-

isfactory method of curing the men of the unpleasant habit of swearing, one may be sure.

Brimstone Bill was the worst offender in camp
this way—that was how he had earned his name
—but after spring came that year he was just about
the mildest-spoken man in seven states. He had
cussed so much during the cold weather that several times he had been nearly covered up and
smothered by the frozen words and had to be
pulled out from under the heap he had made.
When spring came and he had to listen to all of
his words as they thawed out—ah! there was some
real excitement, most assuredly! He was deaf for
three weeks afterwards, and he never did fully
recover from the dreadful things he had heard.
His experience completely cured him of swearing,
however, and ever afterwards—whenever he began
to feel the old inclination to say words of such nature—he would relieve his feelings with whistling
instead.

The weather kept on growing colder and colder,
and finally Paul heard a rumor that it had grown
so cold that the Pacific Ocean had frozen over.
The story seemed so unlikely that he decided to
investigate for himself. "I'm going to see if it's
true, what they say about the Pacific being frozen," he explained to his men, "and also I'm so
homesick for the sight of some regular old white

snow that I'm going to look around a little and see if I can't find some." So, followed by the faithful Babe, he set out on snowshoes to the westward.

He kept on going until he came to the ocean, but not a flake of white snow could he glimpse anywhere. The ice on the Pacific looked pretty solid, and so he struck out across it, always on the lookout for some snow that wasn't blue. He kept on and kept on, but he was far into China before he found any white snow. Proof of this may be found in the fact that nothing but white snow has ever fallen in central China. Paul was so pleased over finding what he was looking for that he loaded Babe with all he could carry and set off for home again.

When he finally got back to camp again his men all held a tremendous celebration, so pleased were they at the sight of familiar, old-fashioned snow again. Paul gave each of them a white snowball for a Christmas present that year, and most of them carried theirs around in their pockets for many years thereafter as proof that they had spent the Winter of the Blue Snow in Paul's camp. Then, if anyone doubted their word, they would just pull their white snowball out of their pocket, and there could be no further doubt about their telling the truth.

It was while the Blue Snow was on the ground that the Snow Wassets were nearly exterminated by Paul's men. The Snow Wasset is unlike other animals, inasmuch as it hibernates during the summer instead of the winter. When the snow begins to melt as the weather turns warm in the spring, this queer animal grows a pair of strong front legs that end in paws armed with big digging claws. Its color changes to green, and by the time the last snowdrift has melted away, it is denned up, all snug and sound, in a hole which it has dug in the ground. There, all covered over with moss and dirt, it sleeps away until winter comes again, when it wakes up as the first snow begins to fall. By the time drifts have begun to deepen, it has shed its legs and green fur, and has grown a brand-new winter coat. Its new fur is of the purest white and is very valuable, but as the animal is thus so colored that it cannot be seen as it wallows about in the snow, it is very seldom ever captured.[1]

During the Winter of Blue Snow, however, the

[1] The Wasset moves about only when it has deep snow to travel in, and it gets from place to place by dipping and squirming through the drifts. It soon attains remarkable skill in this method of travel, which enables it to sneak up through the snow under crouching rabbits, skulking foxes or even wolves and drag its prey kicking down below the surface, there to be devoured. Indians used to use the Wasset's winter skin in making canoes; there being no leg holes in the pelt, it was peculiarly well adapted to the making of such crafts.

Wasset could be easily seen, white against the blue, and Paul's men put in much of their time that winter in hunting the squirming creatures as they played among the blue drifts. Johnny Inkslinger sold many Wasset skins in the spring, and the high price he received for these rare pelts did much toward making up to Paul for the poor cut of timber during the winter.

The winter was long, but at last it came to an end, the snow melted off and all the frozen words were thawed out. It was then that Paul Bunyan made a big raft of what logs had been cut and started floating down the river to deliver them. Somehow or other, he and his men got completely lost on the way, and they floated on and on without ever finding out where they were. They ran out of food and had to live on a diet of frogs' legs for several weeks, when finally and very strangely they found themselves right back at where they had started. They had floated with the river as it made a perfect circle, and to this day this exploit of Paul's is known as the Great Circle Drive. It is, in fact, the only circle drive that has ever been made.

The Circle Drive disgusted Paul with the Big Onion River. "I'll make no more use of it," he declared. "From now on we'll drag all of our logs to the Mississippi River and make our drives down it, for I'll never send another drive down the Big Onion." And so it was that he cared not a bit when, a few days later, a great tree was accidentally felled into the Big Onion and splashed all the water out of the river.

In the Lake States Paul had found the trees to be the biggest he had ever seen. They gave him the best chance he had yet had of using his big crosscut saw and, in fact, the trees were so big that ordinary men with ordinary tools could make but little impression on them. That had been discovered when he had sent out two monster crews, in addition to the Seven Axmen, hoping to make a record cut. The Seven Axmen, of course, did their work with their usual ease in spite of the size of the trees, but the two crews got into an amusing tangle. They worked hard for a week, each man chopping away for all he was worth, before they discovered that they were all hewing away on different parts of the same tree.

So big were these trees that when Paul wanted to see to the top of one of them, he had to call out all of his men to help him look. So it was not strange that one day when one of these great trees fell into the Big Onion it splashed all the water out of the river bed. The water was splashed so far that two settlers established farms in the bed of the stream and had their crops all ready for harvesting before the water finally ran back and washed all their possessions away. Paul Bunyan certainly did a wise thing in giving up all thought of trying to make use of this treacherous stream, as one could never tell what it was going to do next. After he started skidding his logs to the Mississippi his bad luck left him, and he began to get ahead with his logging operations as he had planned and in a greater way than ever before.

It was about this time that he invented the Round Turn, which is still in use, no better one ever having been devised. Turning the Great Blue Ox about had always been a lot of trouble, as Paul had always done it simply by picking up Babe and setting him down again headed in the other direction. He got tired of doing this so many times every day, and at last he figured out a new method. He taught Babe to walk in a small half-circle so that when he stopped he was headed back in the opposite direction. This was the Round Turn, whereby an animal or team turns *itself* around instead of being lifted around, and it was such a sensible way that it is still in use. Nowadays, very few people follow Paul's old method of turning their work animals about.

After Paul Bunyan had started using the Mississippi River for floating his logs to the mills, he one time made a mistake. He had received an order for a drive of logs from a big sawmill down near the mouth of the river, below New Orleans. The logs were made into a big raft, and Paul sent a crew of his men along to deliver it to the mill. When they reached their destination, they found the mill owner had changed his mind and that he refused to accept the logs unless the price was made much lower than had been agreed. He, of course, thought that nothing else could be done except to take what he offered, since the logs were where they were and it would be almost impossible to get them upstream again.

Paul was not the man to be cheated in this way, however, and as soon as he received this message from his men, he determined to get the logs back and fool the rascally mill owner. He thought over the matter for a while and then went out to where Babe and Bessie were feeding. He gave each of them a hogshead or two of salt, which they gulped down greedily, and then he led them away to the upper waters of the river. The salt which they had swallowed made the two animals very thirsty, indeed, and by the time they reached the banks of the Mississippi they were eager for a long drink. Paul grinned as he turned them loose and let them begin to quench their thirst.

They stood out in the water and drank and drank and drank, and so much did they swallow

The Splinter Cats were always a little dazed after smashing a tree trunk into bits, as anyone can easily understand

and so fast did they suck up the water that the current of the river began flowing back upstream to where they were. They kept on drinking faster than ever, so thirsty were they, and together the Great Blue Ox and the Yaller Cow drank so much that finally the big log raft floated back upstream on the current that ran backwards up the river. Thus Paul got back his logs and nothing was lost by the transaction excepting a few hogsheads of salt.

The Little Chore Boy had meanwhile been promoted from the grindstone, and given the job of cutting the firewood for the cook shanty. He did his work so slowly, though, that at last Paul sent him back to his former work and rigged up a mechanical firewood saw to take the youngster's place. His new invention ran perfectly, and the speed with which it worked fascinated Paul so greatly that he was nearly buried in the sawdust from it when Ole found him and aroused him to save himself from being smothered. It was a near escape, and Paul always guarded against such a thing happening again whenever the saw was running.

It was in Wisconsin that the last of the Splinter Cats was caught and killed. These great animals used to be quite common in the big woods until

Paul Bunyan grew irritated over the amount of good timber they destroyed and began to exterminate them. The Splinter Cat was especially fond of honey and wild bees, hives of which were frequently found in hollow trees in the woods. Its method of finding its favorite food was simple but very destructive, and for that reason the great logger's anger fell upon it.

The Splinter Cat was a very queer-looking animal, with long, strong legs and with claws on its feet to aid in climbing trees. Its legs were built like coiled steel springs, and so powerful were they that they hurled the creature tremendously hard whenever it made a leap. Its most peculiar feature, though, was its head, which was exceedingly heavy and hard, just like the end of a battering ram. When it became hungry, the Splinter Cat would climb into a tall tree, and from this vantage point it would leap as strongly as it could against the trunk of another tree nearby, hitting the tree with its hard head and crashing against it with such force that the trunk would be shattered into splinters. Thus it got its name of Splinter Cat. It would continue shattering trees in this manner until by chance and the process of elimination it finally found a bee tree in its smashing course. Bursting this open in its peculiar way, it would feed on the bees and honey until satisfied and then hide away for a long nap.[2]

The Splinter Cat worked only at night and was especially active during heavy storms. For that reason it was seldom seen, but often when a hard wind was blowing the loggers used to hear the crashing and crackling of trees in the forest that told of the Splinter Cat making its rounds. It destroyed so much good timber in its search for food, often laying waste to great stretches of forest during a single stormy night, that Paul decided to rid the woods of all Splinter Cats. He taught Elmer to lie in wait for them among the trees at night, following the crashing sounds they made until he caught one of them on the ground just after it had splintered a tree. The poor animals were always a little dazed for a few moments after smashing a tree trunk into bits with their heads, as anyone can easily understand, and it was at this helpless stage that Elmer would pounce upon them and destroy them. So expert did the great Moose Terrier become in his Splinter Cat hunting

[2] Despite Paul's warfare on the species, now and then evidence is discovered to show that the Splinter Cat is still occasionally creating destruction among the forests. Appalling waste has been wrought by this animal, but such is the present-day ignorance of its habits that its work, in the shape of a wrecked forest, has usually been ascribed to wind storms or lightning.

that it was not very long before they were about done away with, and finally Paul himself killed the last one after his dog had dragged it into camp still alive.

Paul Bunyan's operations in the Lake States became more and more widespread, and each year his crews grew larger and larger and cut more timber than the year before. Finally, after the biggest year he had ever known, Paul floated his Great Drive of logs to the mills. There were so many logs in this drive that they formed a big jam across the Mississippi River and stopped the flow of water for almost two weeks. The jam was at last broken and the logs delivered without any further trouble.

After his Great Drive, Paul Bunyan's work in the Lake States was done, for this drive had included nearly the last of the good timber to be found in all that section of the country. Only small patches were left here and there, and the great logger was already making plans for locating in an entirely new part of the country. His next move was to the Pacific coast, but before he made definite arrangements for starting on this new migration westward, his affairs in the Big Onion Camp had to be straightened up, his men paid off and his various possessions there packed for carrying away. Also, there was the big celebration to be held before the breakup of the camp, in celebration of the completion of the most successful season of logging work that had ever been known.

XIII

The Breakup of the
Big Onion Camp

AFTER the Great Drive had been delivered down
river, all the men assembled again at the Big
Onion Camp to receive their pay and to attend to
other various duties which must precede the clos-
ing of the camp. All were sorry that Paul Bunyan
had finished his logging work in the Lake States,
for they had enjoyed their work there and had
helped in the performance of some mighty deeds
that are still talked about.

The camp was a very busy place while everyone was making ready for the breakup. There was
the sound of the tireless scratching of Johnny Inkslinger's pen as he made out thousands of pay
checks; there was the scrambling around of all the
men who were cleaning up the camp—for Paul,
like any good woodsman, would never leave any

rubbish or dirt behind him when he moved on; there was the rattling of pots and pans in the cook shanty where the cooks were making ready for the big Sunday dinner that always marked the end of a season's work; and then, too, there could be heard a continual and prodigious scraping and grunting, accompanied by a shrill whistling, out behind the stables where Brimstone Bill and his crew of helpers were busily engaged in giving Babe and Bessie their annual spring cleaning.

Brimstone Bill had long ago been given charge of the two faithful animals—taking Ole's job after the smithy had begun to demand all of the Big Swede's time—and he used to grow quite profane over the hard work which caring for the two big creatures demanded. However, since his experience during the Winter of the Blue Snow, he no longer used words that had even a harsh sound, but relieved his feelings by whistling, instead. Just now, engaged as he was in the trying task of removing a whole year's accumulation from two such prodigious creatures as Babe and Bessie, he whistled continuously as he worked, and the shrill sound of his tootling could be heard throughout the entire camp.

Scouring up the Great Blue Ox was no easy task, one may be sure, and the Yaller Cow was almost as bad. It took three tons of strong soap, a lake

THE BREAKUP OF THE BIG ONION CAMP

full of water and forty barrels of hair tonic to get
the enormous Babe into spick and span condition
and almost as much for Bessie. Then, after the cleaning was all done, the Ox and Cow had to be given
their special holiday dinner—an extra allowance of
baled hay—and that, too, was a lot of trouble.

The two big animals were ordinarily fed a ration of baled hay only once a week, feeding on
pine branches the rest of the time, but at the end
of the drive in the spring they were always given
an extraordinarily big feed of hay as a reward for
their faithful work during the winter. When Brimstone Bill fed baled hay to his charges, the great
creatures would chew up two or three bales to a
mouthful, and the baling wires often caused them
a lot of trouble. While they were eating, several
men always had to stand nearby with pitchforks
and crowbars to pick the wires from between
their teeth every now and then, when they became
all tangled up after a dozen bales or so. So it was
no wonder, with all this work ahead of him, that
Bill was whistling away as hard as he possibly
could while he was getting well started on his
task.

Meanwhile, all the men were looking forward
with great expectations to the big dinner that
would be served to them on the morrow, and Paul
was happy to see them in such high spirits. His

feelings changed somewhat, though, when Hot Biscuit Slim came to him with an unwelcome bit of bad news.

"Mr. Bunyan," the chief cook began, "them cow fellers from Texas ain't showed up yet with that drove of five thousand steers that was to be here in time for the dinner tomorrow, and so we're mighty short of meat. I've got plenty of everything else, but not near enough meat. Mebbe you had better send out Shot Gunderson to kill some wild game, seein' as how that is about the only chanct we have of gettin' meat for the dinner."

"I'll not only send him out, but I'll go hunting myself," promised Paul, rather worried by the news the cook had brought. "My men are all looking forward to that dinner, and I'll not disappoint them, even though I have to run down every deer in the country."

Calling the Little Chore Boy to him, he sent the lad scurrying after his shotgun and rifle, his ammunition pouch and his hunting coat, as well as the pair of light running boots which he always wore when he went hunting. He found Shot Gunderson and gave him his instructions, and then as soon as the Chore Boy returned from his errand with the equipment, Paul himself was ready to start out. Calling Elmer, his Moose Terrier, to him he set off. Happening by chance to pass by where

Brimstone Bill was working, he stopped to chat for a moment or two.

Upon hearing of the meatless condition of the camp, Bill scratched his head and offered a helpful suggestion. "There's *whistle* Bessie, the *whistle, whistle!* Yaller Cow, now," he mentioned hopefully. "She'd make a *whistle* whole heapin' hocus of *whistle* good beef, I *whistle, whistle* betcha!" He didn't care much for the cow, as he had to milk her every day, and he didn't like the job.

But Paul only laughed. "You'll have to get a better idea than that, Bill," he said. "Bessie is too useful and too much of a pet to be made into steaks. Besides, she would probably be too tough and couldn't be eaten anyhow," and with another laugh he turned away, leaving behind him a Brimstone Bill who was doing his best to whistle his disappointment away.

Meanwhile, Shot Gunderson had saddled his bear and set off in the other direction from that taken by Paul. Shot always rode his big pet bear when he went hunting, and the animal was a very large one and could carry him along much faster than he could have run on his own legs. Shot had broken him to the saddle a long while before this and had made quite a pet of him. Whenever he got to where there was a lot of game, he would unsaddle the animal and turn him loose, and so well was the bear trained that he would help his master kill a herd of moose, or run down a deer, or catch whatever other game was to be found. Thus, through his pet's help, Shot was always able to bring in a lot of prizes when he went hunting.

This time the bear galloped for a long distance with Shot on his back before any signs of game were found. Then all at once the stiff bristles on the bear's back rose so suddenly that they threw Shot right out of his saddle. He didn't mind that, as this was his pet's usual method of letting him know that they were approaching close to a herd of some kind of game. So the hunter unsaddled his bear, hung the saddle on a limb, and together master and animal crept along to surprise whatever was ahead of them.

Suddenly there was a loud fierce growl from right in front of them, answered by a more ferocious one from behind and then by a chorus of others all around, and so terrible did they sound that Shot would probably have run away if he hadn't had his pet bear with him for protection. He had blundered right into the middle of a big herd of wild bears, great enormous fierce fellows, different from any that are now known, which used to run together in big droves and attack anything they came to. They growled and they roared, and the sound was so terrible that any ordinary hunter would have sunk right down into the ground. Then suddenly they all started for Shot and his tame bear at the same time.

Shot was so busy firing and loading and firing again for a few minutes that he didn't have a chance to see how his pet was making out, but when he did look around he saw that all the bears were dead—a hundred or more of them—except one that was worrying the throat of an animal just breathing his last gasp.

"That ought to be enough b'ar meat for the dinner tomorrow," Shot said to himself, and he started back to get his saddle, glad that his pet and he had come through the great fight safely. "I guess I'd better hurry on back to camp and send the teamsters out after all this meat," he decided and hastened to saddle up his tame bear again. He had quite a little trouble in doing this, as the bear was more fractious than he had ever been before. The big fight and the taste of blood had stirred him up too much, his master thought, and it took several hard and well-placed kicks to quiet the animal down so that he could be mounted.

He traveled very roughly, too, all the way back to camp, but Shot kept a tight rein on him and kept promising him all kinds of punishment when they got to their destination. They arrived at last, however, and teamsters were sent out without any delay to bring the meat into camp.

It was not until then that Shot Gunderson discovered that the bear he had ridden back to camp was not his pet at all, but a strange animal entirely. His own bear must have been killed in the fight, and in his hurry to get back to camp he had saddled and ridden one of the fierce wild ones! Shot grieved a great deal over the loss of his pet after he discovered what a mistake he had made.

As for Paul, he traveled a great distance and saw not a sign of any game. He had almost begun to despair when a great flock of fool-hens, or spruce partridges, settled down around him. They settled on the boughs of the trees so thickly that they were crowded together on their perches as tightly as they could get, and there were so many of them that he hardly knew how to go about getting them. He was too close to use his shotgun without tearing them all to pieces, and his rifle would kill only a few with each shot.

Finally he settled the matter in a very clever way. He took his rifle bullets and punched holes in them and then tied a long piece of fishing line to each bullet through the holes he had made. The first shot he fired he aimed along a limb where five or six hundred partridges were sitting all in a row and pulled the trigger. The bullet which he had fixed up so nicely just followed along that limb entirely through every one of those birds, carrying the fishing line with it, so that all Paul had to do was to tie the ends of the line together and sling the necklace of partridges over his shoulder. He kept on stringing partridges that way until finally they became scared, and what few were left flew away. By that time, however, he was pretty well loaded down with birds, and he looked almost like a ball of feathers as he walked along.

He was far from satisfied with his success, though. Birds were all right as appetizers, he felt, but he knew his men would prefer to stick their teeth into strong red meat.

After a while he came on some deer tracks where a large herd of the animals had passed. Big tracks they were, the biggest deer tracks he had ever seen. Elmer sniffed along, following the trail at full speed, and Paul ran along behind him, glad that at last he was within reach of the meat he wanted for the big dinner tomorrow.

He followed those deer tracks all the way across northern Wisconsin and Michigan. Then suddenly they doubled back westward again, he and Elmer following right after them, but not until sundown did he get close enough to the herd that was making them to take a shot. There was a wise old buck at the head of that herd, and he almost bested Paul. Elmer got along all right on that chase, as he was always resting one pair of legs while he ran on the other pair, but Paul—with his heavy equipment, his big load of birds and his one pair of legs that ran continuously without any chance for rest—came near being fagged out by the time he finally began to catch up with the deer.

They were already back past the place where the chase had started, and the deer were running more slowly by this time. But Paul was also running more slowly, and so he sent Elmer on ahead to turn the herd while he sat down to wait until his dog drove the animals back past him. And pretty soon here they came, the whole herd of them, one after the other and in such formation that he was able to bring down every one of them. They were all extraordinarily big deer, weighing close to a thousand pounds apiece, it is said, and Paul felt rather proud of his success.

When he saw their exceptional size and counted how very many of them there were, he knew that the big dinner on the morrow would not lack for meat. Cramming a part of the animals into the big pockets of his hunting coat and slinging the rest over his shoulders, he set out for camp, glad to be carrying in such a good bag from the day's hunting.

It was night when he finally got back to camp, and as he came near he saw in the moonlight a strange dark shape reaching high in the air. It had not been there that morning, and he was quite puzzled as to what it could be. At last he came to it, and one may imagine his astonishment at discovering it to be a huge pile of gigantic bears. They were stacked up like logs, and around the base of the pile Hot Biscuit Slim and hundreds of assistants were working away butchering bear meat for all they were worth.

"Good for Shot Gunderson," roared Paul, greatly pleased, when he was told that the hunter was responsible for bringing in the big furry creatures. "It certainly looks as though he has been enjoying some good hunting. And here, Slim, is more meat, to make a little variety," and he dumped down his own prodigious load of deer and partridges while the chief cook sent cook-boys scurrying away for another crew of helpers.

"Do your best, Slim," Paul said, "for tomorrow is to be your day of glory," and hugely delighted that everything was turning out so well, the big logger hurried to the bunkhouse to congratulate his fellow hunter. What a shout of laughter he let forth when he heard the story of Shot Gunderson's experience with the wild bear!

All of the men in camp knew of the big dinner

to be given on the morrow, and so all of them had decided to save up a good appetite for it by eating nothing until it should be put on the table. Thus, having no meals except the one grand one to think about, all the cooks worked with special effort all that night and half the next day in preparing their masterpiece. Through the long hours the fire-tenders industriously piled wood on their roaring fires, kettles steamed, spit-boys grew red as beets from the heat as they turned thousands of sizzling roasts of bear ham and deer haunch, oven doors clanged, and cooks and pot-rustlers dashed hither and yon with tireless energy.

The air was so full of wonderful odors that not a man in camp slept that night, but each just lay back in his bunk, spread his face in a broad grin of delicious anticipation, and inhaled the matchless smells that every breath brought to him. The blower had been turned on full blast, and it worked overtime in bringing its great load of appetizing aroma from the kitchens to the bunkhouse.

As the time drew towards noon the next day, the men began to get restless and finally began to congregate before the big doors of the mess hall. So fast did the crowd grow that within a few moments the last comers were several miles away, though they had pushed as close as they could get.

There were so many men in Paul's camp that only once did he ever try to count them. That time the government had asked him for a census of his camp, and so he put a special counting crew out through the camp to find out how many men there were. They had little success, though, as the men were going and coming all the time and mixed up the counting crew so badly that they lost all track of what they were doing. Paul finally got a pretty accurate set of figures by counting the number of flapjacks that were made each morning for breakfast. Figuring an average of sixty hot cakes per man, he was able to estimate very closely the total number of men in his camp. He knew that all were sure to be on hand when the flapjacks were served, just as now every man was present for the big Sunday dinner.

At last the cooks began testing the big soup hose, and the doors were thrown open. The men poured in like water rushing through a broken dam, and every man was in his place as the soup hose began to squirt the first course. Such a whisper of soup sipping as rushed through the place as the men began to ply their spoons! It was like the sound of a gale blowing through the branches of a pine woods.

By the time the soup bowls were pushed aside, heavily loaded trains began to move along the tracks between the rows of tables, and from the cars the waiters expertly slid filled plates before the men. As these plates were each six feet across, and loaded with all the food that could be piled on them, it was no easy task to slide them safely into place. In Paul's camp only the steadiest and the strongest men were able to work as waiters.

As the men ate, the sound of crackling partridge bones made one think of a forest of bee trees assailed by a band of Splinter Cats. The trains and waiters passed back and forth many times, and every time an empty plate could be seen another filled one was passed down to take its place.

Such appetites did they have, and so wonderful was the food served them, that the men ate five times as long as they had ever eaten before, and at last there was no sound around the tables except that of hard breathing. Then, one by one, they staggered to their feet, waddled slowly toward the bunkhouse, and climbed into their bunks, where they fell back in a delightful stupor.

A week or so later, after they had come to life again and when all were on their feet once more, Paul Bunyan hesitated no longer about breaking camp. He passed each man his pay check and away they all went, straggling along with their turkeys on their shoulders, all able to talk of nothing except the great Sunday dinner which had marked the end of the Big Onion Camp.

Paul gathered together all the bales of tools and other equipment which had been packed up ready for removal, loaded them on Babe's back, and set off for his farm and family. He was accompanied only by the Seven Axmen, the Little Chore Boy, the faithful Ole and just a few others from his great crew of followers.

XIV

Paul Bunyan's Farm

ALL during these later years of his lumbering, Paul Bunyan had owned a fine farm about which many interesting tales are told. Here it was that his family stayed while he was in the woods. Here it was, also, that the great logger spent most of his time every year after the spring drive was over and up until it was time to get into the woods again in the fall. Here, during the summer, he would reward Babe, Bessie and his other animals by turning them out in his rich pastures.

Paul amused himself occasionally by conducting various experiments with growing things. Once he tried raising macaroni, planting nearly his whole farm in macaroni, but there must have been something wrong with his seed. When his macaroni came up, it kept on growing and growing until half of just one stalk would have fed a section gang for a week. Finally, it stopped growing and ripened off to the prettiest creamy macaroni color anyone ever saw, but that didn't cheer Paul up any for he thought he was going to lose a lot of money on his macaroni because of its being so big.

Johnny Inkslinger saved him from that, however. Johnny wrote to all the big factories back East and kept after them until he sold every one of them a stalk of Paul's macaroni for a smokestack.

In addition to the great logger's pet animals which have been mentioned before, he had another one which he kept on the farm and never used in any of his logging work. This was the Roan Colt. Paul had high hopes at first of making a race horse out of the Colt, and in order to give him the proper training he built a big race track on the farm. This track was only five miles around, as Paul thought that was enough distance to start with, but the Colt was able to run on it only two days.

When he first started out, he ran so fast that he kicked dirt back in his own face, and before two days were up he had worn the track down to such a depth that water was running into it in great streams. After that Paul had to use his race track for a duck-pond, and he had to give up all of his racing ambitions for the Roan Colt for fear the animal would likewise ruin every other track he might run on.

Paul's daughter, however, made good use of the

Ole staggered into sight carrying one of Babe's shoes,
sinking to his knees in the ground at every step

ruined race track. Teenie, as she was named, had charge of all the poultry around the farm, and she was so smart about her work that she made quite a bit of money from it. Her daddy gave her the race track for a duck-pond, and her flock of ducks was the finest that could be found anywhere.

At first the ducks laid eggs of just ordinary duck-egg size, but Teenie fooled them into doing much better than that. She got Ole to help her, and together they chipped out a big stone in the shape of an enormous big egg so perfect that it would have fooled any one—even a duck. The only flaw about it was that the stone wasn't quite as big as the egg started out to be, so that the ends were flat on account of not having enough stone to round them off. Teenie was a little worried at first for fear that this defect might keep her plan from working, but later it proved of great advantage.

When this big egg was put into the duck house where all could see it, it certainly aroused a lot of excitement. The ducks quacked the matter over and over among themselves until finally they began to get quite jealous of any duck that could lay an egg like that. Their duck pride would not allow them to be outdone in a matter of that kind, and so before very long they were all laying real eggs just a little bit bigger than the imitation one. They even copied the flat ends, which was a good thing, for otherwise one of those eggs could never have been taken through any doorway. Paul always admired big things, and he gave Teenie a lot of praise for her success with her ducks.

The feature that Paul Bunyan's farm is most famed for, however, is his great cornstalk. He had a big cornfield on the farm, and all the corn planted there behaved in the usual way, excepting one grain that must have been of a very special kind. When this grain sprouted, it grew so fast that by the time Paul got home that spring no one could see to the top of it.

Paul decided that the best thing to do would be to get rid of it before it grew any taller, and so he gave orders to the Seven Axmen to cut it down. They first tried sawing it down with the great crosscut saw, but it was growing upwards so fast all the time that it just jerked the saw right out of their hands.

Then they tried chopping it down with their axes, but it kept on growing faster than ever, and they could never hit it twice in the same place so as to take out a chip. By the time they could draw back their axes and strike the second time the mark of their first stroke would have grown out of sight above their heads.

Paul began to see that the matter was getting serious, and he tried to think of some other way

of getting the best of the troublesome stalk of corn.
At last he had an idea that looked like the proper
one, and he called all his helpers to him to help
work it out. "Big Charley," he said to the oldest
and biggest of the Seven Axmen, "I want you to
take a big coil of strong rope and climb up the
stalk until you get near the top. Then tie one end
of the rope to the stalk, drop the other end down
so we can grab hold of it, and then we'll bend
the whole thing down to the ground by pulling
on the rope. I'm thinking that I'll bury the top part,
and then let the stalk do all the growing it wants
to right back into the earth. Then if it keeps on
growing as fast as it has been doing so far, the
Chinese will have it to worry about instead of us."

"All right, boss, if you say so," answered Big
Charley, rather doubtfully. "I'm game, but it
doesn't look like a very good plan to me." With
some grumbling and many pessimistic shakes of
his head, he fixed up a big coil of rope, swung it
over his shoulder and started climbing up the
stalk. He finally got to the top all right, but by
that time the stalk had grown so much that the
rope would no longer reach to the ground.

"I knew it wouldn't work," growled Big Charley
to himself. "I guess now that I had better be
getting back down to the ground and tell the boss
that he'd do best to get either a new idea or a

longer rope." Disgusted with the whole plan, he started to slide back down the stalk, but to his surprise and anger, it kept growing upward faster than he could slide the other way. No matter how fast he went down, he was still going up all the time, for the stalk of corn kept carrying him higher and higher and farther away from the ground and food.

Down below Paul had waited for the rope to hang down within his reach, and when he saw it with its lower end dangling far above his head he began to have a suspicion of what had happened. When many hours had passed and Big Charley did not return to earth, he feared for the safety of the Axman and presently figured out the reason for his not appearing. It was well that he did so, or else the man up the stalk might have starved to death before ever he reached the ground again.

"He must be getting mighty hungry by this time," said Paul to the others. "I'll have to get food to him in some way, before he starves. Chore Boy, just you run into the house and get my big shot-gun for me," and within a few minutes the Little Chore Boy laid the weapon in his hands.

The gun was of such a tremendous size that none but he dared fire it, and it had to have a tremendous load in order to perform properly. Usually Paul loaded it with a washtub full of blasting powder and a wheelbarrow load of bricks, but this time, instead of the bricks, he rammed her full of doughgod biscuits. Then he took careful aim up the stalk and shot the biscuits up to Charley.

He kept on feeding Charley in this way until the ears of corn began to develop on the big stalk. One morning, when he came out to shoot the unfortunate Axman's breakfast up to him, he found a number of fresh corncobs scattered on the ground around the roots of the stalk. As all the grains were cleanly gnawed off the cobs, he knew that Charley had now found food of his own, and so was in no further danger of starvation.

It was about this time that the commanding officer from the United States Naval Station on Lake Michigan came to see Paul. He was all dressed up in his fine uniform, with a lot of ribbons pinned on his chest, which he stuck out like a pouter pigeon as he walked. "Are you the owner of this cornstalk?" he asked, very importantly, when he came up to the big logger.

"I sure wish someone else would claim it," Paul laughed in reply.

"Well, sir, I have orders for you to cut it down at once," said the officer, not knowing that Paul was trying his hardest to figure out a way to do that very thing.

The big logger just grinned at his visitor. "As far as that goes," he answered, "your orders have nothing to do with me. Not even the President himself could make me cut that stalk down until I get ready to do so."

A look of deep concern spread over the officer's face. "But the roots of this cornstalk go down deep and spread out so far that they reach in under Lake Michigan on the east and up under Lake Superior on the north, and they are sucking up the water so fast that navigation is being seriously interfered with. Unless the stalk is cut down, and that at once, very soon no boats at all will be able to run on any of the lakes."

Paul nodded his head in agreement. "You didn't let me finish what I started out to say," he told the officer. "I said that nothing could make me cut that stalk down until I got ready to do so, but I'll be ready and mighty glad to get rid of it just as soon as I can figure out how to do away with the pesky thing. I've tried cutting it down, but it grows too fast for us to make any impression on it," and he explained all that had been done.

Suddenly his eyes brightened as a new thought came to him. "Ah, I've got the right plan now," he exclaimed, and strode over to where Ole, the Big Swede, had just staggered into sight carrying one of Babe's shoes toward the smithy.

Now one of the Great Blue Ox's shoes was just like a horseshoe, except that it was many thousand times bigger, and the one Ole was carrying weighted him down so heavily that he sank to his knees in the ground at every step. It took a whole carload of iron just to put new calks on a shoe for Babe, and whenever the Great Blue Ox had to be reshod on all four feet a new iron mine had to be opened. Thus what Paul had in mind was perfectly possible.

The great logger grabbed the big shoe from Ole and carried it back to where the officer was standing. "I'll just put this shoe around the stalk, like a ringer around the peg in playing horseshoes," he explained, "and then twist the ends together so tightly that the flow of sap up the stalk will be shut off. That should make it stop growing so fast, and perhaps give us a chance to cut it down." He proceeded to do the thing as he had said, but there wasn't enough room left, after the shoe had been passed around the stalk, to allow the ends to be twisted together as he had outlined.

However, Paul thought the principle of the plan was the proper one for solving the problem, and he looked around for something else he could use. There was an old logging railroad within ten miles or so of his farm, and from it he ripped up a number of miles of steel track, pulled loose the ties,

[191]

and twisted several strands of the track together into a long cable.

The naval officer was the most astonished man in the world as he watched Paul Bunyan pass this great cable around the base of the big cornstalk and knot it into place very quickly and very tightly. "Now," said the big logger, "that ought to shut off the sap and slow down its growth."

They all waited breathlessly, their eyes straining to see if they could find some evidence of the stalk's growth having stopped. Suddenly the Big Swede gave a loud yell, jumped high in the air as he clicked his heels together, and shouted, "She bane stop! Yumpin' yeeminy! We cut her down quick now, I betcha!" and he ran wildly about looking for an ax.

Surely enough the cable had done the work, and the cornstalk had at last stopped growing. Paul was fully as delighted as the others, and he set his men to chopping away at the big cornstalk while he worked out another problem, that of saving the Axman who had been up the stalk all summer.

He soon figured out a way whereby Big Charley could be gotten to the ground before the choppers finished their task. He got out his big shotgun again, but instead of loading it this time with biscuits, he crammed into its barrel a big bundle which was wrapped tight like a ball. Luckily a circus was playing nearby, and using its biggest tent, he had constructed a parachute, which he now proceeded to shoot up the stalk to the Axman. Along with the parachute he sent a note, explaining the situation and warning Big Charley to take to flight at once.

So now, feeling sure that Charley was safe, Paul urged his men on to greater efforts. He sent Ole five miles away to look up through a powerful telescope at the top of the stalk and send word to him at once upon seeing in which direction it would fall after the cutting had weakened it. He wanted to know which way it would fall in order to warn all the people in its path and direct them to safety.

Finally the Little Chore Boy rushed into view, breathing hard from having run so fast. "The Big Swede says the top is beginning to lean towards the west," he panted. It was well that it had chosen that direction in which to fall, as there were fewer people to the westward which it might endanger in its rush to the ground.

The stalk began to fall, and there could be heard the sound of the wind whistling through its leaves and tassel far, far above. As soon as his ears caught this noise, Paul sprang into his wagon to which Jerry and Jinny, his Mule Team, were hitched and impatiently waiting to go. He gave them their heads, and away they galloped to the west, almost as fast as lightning. So fast did they go that they could be seen only when Paul slowed them down to a walk when passing the word of warning to some one in the danger zone. A mighty ride that was, and one that should be more widely famous.

For two and a half days the big stalk continued to fall before it finally hit the ground. After the dust had cleared away, Paul sent men out with surveying instruments to measure its size, but they were unable to get the exact and original figures. In falling, most of it had been raveled out by the rushing of the wind, and the few miles of it that remained intact were a poor indicator in determining its exact size.

Some idea of its hugeness, however, can be had from knowing what kind of ears of corn it had on it. One ear was driven by the force of the fall right straight down into the earth. It stuck there so tight that Paul couldn't get it out even when he hitched the Great Blue Ox to it. He brought up his Mule Team to help Babe pull, and when the three animals tugged away altogether, something just had to give way. But even then only the cob of the ear was pulled out of the ground, leaving the grains still in the earth. It is said that the ear made a hole in the ground sixty feet across, and that the loose grains that were left after the cob was pulled out filled this to such a depth that no one ever did find out how far it went down into the earth. Luckily none of the grains ever sprouted to make other cornstalks like their parent.

Big Charley floated with his parachute for two weeks before he finally landed, and then he came to earth a thousand miles from where Paul's farm was. He endured many hardships before he finally got back to where he had started from, and by that time he was so angry over what had happened to him that he made up his mind to leave Paul Bunyan. The big logger offered him a lot of inducements to stay, but he would not change his mind. His six cousins all stuck by him, and together they quit in a huff. They marched away down the road with their turkeys on their shoulders and never a look backward and were never heard of again. They were mighty woodsmen, and their absence was keenly felt by their former boss.

Another thing happened that helped make Paul anxious to give up his farm. Most of the corn he had raised that year was popcorn. One day, after it was all harvested and put in the granary, the building accidentally caught on fire and popped all the corn stored there. The flying white grains flew all over the farm until they covered the ground three or four feet deep, or perhaps even more. It didn't seem to hurt Babe, but all the other animals on the farm—Bessie, the Mule Team, the Roan Colt, and all the others—thought they were having an extraordinarily severe snow blizzard and froze to death. Elmer, the Moose Terrier, was in the house while the popping was going on, and so he also was saved.

The loss of all his animals was quite a blow to Paul, and his loss disgusted him with farming. Only Babe and Elmer were left to him out of all his pets, and he decided to delay no longer about moving to the Pacific coast.

The Seven Axmen were lost, his farm was worn out, the timber was cut, and he was ready to hunt out a new and wilder part of the country. So, with his wife, Teenie and Jean, his son and daughter, a few of his old followers, and Babe and Elmer he set out westward.

Ole, the Big Swede, was faithful to Paul and accompanied him into the Pacific states and so did the Little Chore Boy and Johnny Inkslinger. Also some of his former workmen followed after him later on and joined his western crew, glad to work once more under the greatest boss in the woods.

XV

Paul Bunyan's Last Exploits

I T is regrettable that the records of Paul Bunyan's adventures on the Pacific coast are not
more complete. Not nearly so much is known of
his work there as has been told about his earlier
labors; indeed, only a few stories have come down
to us regarding the great logger's latter years. Such
neglect may, however, seem quite natural when
one considers that it was in the East, in the
Dakotas and in the Lake States, that Paul performed his greatest deeds and carried on the
mightiest logging that the world will ever witness.
Accordingly, historians have been interested prin-
cipally in preserving the records of his work there
and have not had the time to pay much attention
to the lesser things which he accomplished in
Washington and Oregon.

It is said that on his trip westward, several days after leaving the Lake States, Paul became a little careless while thinking over several matters of importance and allowed the sharp end of his heavy peavy to drag on the ground. Holding it loosely with one hand as he walked along absorbed in deep thought, he permitted it to drag for quite a distance before his attention was called to the damage he was doing. Wherever the sharp steel end had scratched along the earth it had dug right down through rock and rubble, making a tremendous gash many miles long and hundreds of feet deep. Paul Bunyan certainly left his mark on that part of the country, and anyone who has seen the Grand Canyon can have no doubts about the size of the great logger, knowing that his peavy made such a mark.

Among the better known of Paul's faithful followers who accompanied him to the Pacific coast was one queer old codger who was named Halfway Hank. Poor Hank had at one time been a most capable lumberjack, until one sad day during the Big Fog when he had been caught and crushed by a falling tree. When he finally recovered from his terrible accident, it was found that only about half of him was left—one arm, one eye and one leg were gone—and so forever afterwards he was known as Halfway. Paul sent the unfortunate jack

out to his farm, and there Hank was put in charge
of the great hives of bees which kept the camps
supplied regularly with the wonderful golden
honey that was always served with Sourdough
Sam's flapjacks.

Halfway Hank had become quite interested in
his new work and very proficient as well, con-
sidering the shape he was in. He developed a surprising agility which aided him greatly as a bee
herder, and so expert did he become before very
long that he could drive his millions of bees to
pasture each morning and back to their hives again
in the evening without losing track of a single one
of his charges. On Paul's trek westward, Halfway
Hank brought up at the rear of the procession, industriously hopping along on his one leg and herd-
ing his bees in a close, humming swarm. He drove
that great swarm of bees entirely across the country, over high mountains, through terrible deserts,
and lost only three bees all the way. At the end
of the journey he claimed that those three would
never have been lost if he hadn't been shy a leg.

Finally, Paul and those with him reached a
section of the country where the timber grew tall
and thick and where the opportunities for logging
seemed almost ideal. It was among the big trees
of Washington or Oregon that the great logger
finally settled after his long journey from the Lake

States, and it was here that he established his new camp.

Here it was, also, that he built his great sawmill. No one knows just why he became interested in owning a sawmill, for he was a man who was never content unless he was out of doors among the trees. Perhaps, though, he built it to be sure of a place where he could dispose of the logs his crews cut and then turned the actual management of it over to Johnny Inkslinger. Or perhaps he built it so as to have a place for testing out the bandsaw, which he invented at this time, and which to a great extent soon replaced the old-fashioned circular saw in the larger mills of the country.

At any rate, Paul Bunyan built his sawmill in one of the Pacific coast states, and a most wonderful mill it was. It was taller than the highest building of that or of any other day, and the bandsaws in it ran from top to bottom, passing through the several hundred floors in turn and sawing logs on every floor. So great was the capacity of this mill that it had to run only one day a week in order to saw up all the timber that could possibly be cut during the rest of the time.

There was a little trouble with it at first, but that was soon fixed. The workmen who put the machinery together originally were rather ignorant of the intricate new contrivances they were handling, and they put the whole mill together backwards. Then, when the power was turned on, the entire mill ran just the opposite of what it should have done, working up sawdust into boards and then back into the original logs, instead of starting out with the logs and ending up with boards and sawdust. Paul let it run this way for a while, until it had worked all the waste shavings and mountains of sawdust in that part of the country into good logs again, and then he tore it down and rebuilt it the right way.

Needless to say, the sawmill worked perfectly after that. It became quite a hobby with Paul, and he equipped it with all kinds of doodads and gadgets and dingfaddles which he invented, until an inventory of its equipment would read like a Sears, Roebuck catalogue.

The only trouble which he had with it after that was with its smokestacks, which were so tall the clouds were always getting tangled around them. Finally he had to equip the smokestacks with hinges and block-and-tackle machinery so that they could be lowered when any especially big clouds had to get by. The little ones didn't worry him any, as he had stationed men on the tops of the smokestacks, and these were able to push off all the smaller clouds with the long poles they held.

It was in the Northwest that Paul decided to make the work a little easier for the Great Blue Ox, and so he bought several thousand yokes of ordinary oxen to assist Babe in pulling heavy loads over the mountains. The oxen didn't last long, however, on account of the miscalculation which someone made in yoking all the animals up together.

Seeing that he had such enormous pulling power to do the work, Paul had fixed up an extra heavy load of logs which he intended to have his animals drag across several mountain ranges and on down to the ocean. When they started out, with the mighty Babe in the lead, there was a long line of yoked oxen as far as the eye could see, stringing down the side of the mountain range and across the valley at its foot and on ahead toward where the next range blocked the way.

Everything went all right until Babe, at the head of the procession, started up the steep slope across on the other side of the valley. Not nearly all the other oxen had as yet come across the crest of the first mountains, and so here they were: a line of them from the mountain top on one side, across the valley and now starting up the mountain on the other side. And that is where the accident happened.

Babe always worked much faster going up hill

than he did any other way, and now, with the long steep slope ahead of him, he speeded up for all he was worth. Before anyone could stop him, he had stretched out that line of oxen high up in the air, tight from the crest of one mountain range to that of the other across the valley. There they hung, just like clothes on a line, and before the Great Blue Ox could be made to back up and lower them to the ground again every ox in the string had been strangled. It is said that Paul's crews were fed on beef for a long time after that.

So Babe continued to do all the hauling alone after that until several years later, when suddenly he began to lose all of his old-time energy and interest in his tremendous tasks. His appetite also failed, and he showed in other ways that old age was upon him. This was not surprising, for the huge animal was more than a hundred years old and had been constantly doing the heaviest kind of labor ever since he was a calf.

Paul saw to it that the Great Blue Ox was given the very best of attention, but all efforts were unavailing toward saving his life. After his death his ribs were used, so some stories tell us, to form the sides of a big locomotive roundhouse in Seattle. Paul would hardly have allowed the remains of his devoted pet to come to so sordid an end, however, and the story that says that the Olympian Mountains are the burial mound of Babe is probably the correct one.

Not long after this Mrs. Paul also passed away. The big logger mourned his double loss greatly, and it seemed from that time on he began to lose his interest in the things he used to do with so much energy and ambition. He had already begun to get very much disgusted over some of the newfangled methods which were being introduced into the woods, replacing some of the better old-fashioned ideas about logging which he had developed. So it wasn't very long before he began to get rid of all his business interests and at last retired from all further lumbering activity.

Having too many people around always irritated Paul, except when he was in a logging camp and the people about him were his own men. Now, even the woods were beginning to get crowded, for many lumbermen were starting operations in the western forests as well as among those still standing further east, and Paul felt that his place was taken by others. With so many trying to do the work which he had done alone and on such a big scale in the olden days, his services were no longer needed.

Taking only his fore-and-aft Moose Terrier, Elmer, and his guns with him, Paul Bunyan one night slipped away from all men who knew him and went far through the thickest woods. There, in the heart of the wildest country that he could find, he put up his shanty, and there he still lives, all alone except for his dog. Men say that he can never die until the last tree is cut down and that until such a time comes, Paul Bunyan and his lone companion will continue to roam the forests.

Once in a while he and Elmer may appear almost any place where there are trees, but as they are always going at a furious pace, it takes sharp eyes to see them at all. They are always running at great speed, chasing down the wild game that is their food. And often, when the winter winds blow harshly, whistling through the trees and moaning down chimneys and around the corners of houses, woodsmen say that these sounds are made by Paul Bunyan calling to his dog as they rush along on their endless hunting.

20